Copying and Duplicating

Photographic and Digital Imaging Techniques

Written by W. Arthur Young, Thomas A. Benson, George T. Eaton, and Joseph Meehan
Edited by Dave Howard

Publication M-1
CAT No. E152 7969
Library of Congress Catalog Card Number 95-72444
ISBN 0-87985-764-1
Printed in the U.S.A.

KODAK is a trademark of Eastman Kodak Company used under license.
DATAGUIDE, DEKTOL, DK-50, DURAFLO, DURATRANS, D-11, D-19, D-76, EASTMAN, EKTACHROME,
EKTACOLOR, EKTAGRAPHIC, EKTAPAN, EKTAPRESS, EKTAR, ESTAR, ESTAR-AH, FLEXICOLOR, GOLD,
HC-110, IMAGELINK, KODACHROME, KODALITH, PANALURE, PLUS-X, POLYCONTRAST, POLYFIBER,
PORTRA, Q-LAB, RADIANCE, READYLOAD, ROYAL, SELECT, SNAP-CAP, TECHNIDOL, T-MAX, TRI-X,
VERICHROME, VERICOLOR, and WRATTEN are trademarks of Eastman Kodak Company.

LICENSED PRODUCT

KODAK Books are published under
license from Eastman Kodak Company by
Silver Pixel Press ®
21 Jet View Drive
Rochester, NY 14624
Fax: (716) 328-5078

COPYING AND DUPLICATING

TABLE OF CONTENTS

Introduction to Copying and Duplicating

The practices of copying and duplicating permit making:

- Multiple copies of photographs when only a print exists.
- Duplicate black-and-white and color negatives to:
  Make old negatives printable.
  Obtain multiple copies of negatives for use in many places.
  Restore historical negatives that are deteriorating so that the images can be preserved.
  Enlarge negatives so that they can be retouched.
  Make negatives where the image quality is enhanced so that quality prints can be made.
- Duplicate color transparencies so that the original transparency can be stored for long-term keeping and the duplicates can be projected or displayed.
- Multiple black-and-white or color negatives or positives for use in many other applications.

The need for copies of photographs, paintings, documents, and other flat reflective originals and transparencies often arises. The commercial, professional, law enforcement, and industrial photographers as well as the advanced amateur, are often called upon to make copies or duplicates of such originals.

Of necessity, we have based the instructions on currently available photographic equipment and on current Kodak films, papers, and chemicals. The reader will want to keep up-to-date on changes and improvements that may be made in these materials.

Products made by manufacturers other than Kodak are mentioned and shown in this publication. The choice of particular products is intended to be representative in nature and is not an endorsement by Kodak for one product as compared with another. Eastman Kodak Company can take no responsibility for products manufactured by other companies.

This publication is intended to provide data and instruction for use of current Kodak products. This is not intended to imply the incompatibility or unsuitability of the products made by other manufacturers. Eastman Kodak Company reserves the right to change and improve its own products. It is good policy to check the information sheets packaged with the product to be sure you have the correct data. The Kodak products described in this publication are available through those dealers normally supplying Kodak products. Equivalent materials may be used if desired.

There are fairly simple ways to make copies and duplicates. Other methods, while more complex, have the potential of making copies and duplicates with improved tone reproductions. Some sensitometry is included in this book to provide an understanding of what happens to tones in the photographic process, and why special copy films such as KODAK Professional Copy Films (black-and-white) and KODAK VERICOLOR Internegative Films (color) give improved tone reproduction when used to copy black-and-white and color originals. Densitometry is introduced as a method of controlling the photographic process.

One of the values of copying and duplicating is to retain the images of old photographs that have started to deteriorate. The copying techniques used in restoration are described in this book, but actual restoration is covered in more detail in *Conservation of Photographs,* Publication F-40. These two books are both needed by the museum workers and others involved with the restoration process.

NOTE: A photographer does not have the unrestricted right to copy everything. Copyright laws restrict the right to make copies to the owners of a copyright. The copyright law as it pertains to the photographer is discussed early in the book.

Explanation of Terms

In most trades or professions, common words are often used in a sense that may be unfamiliar to many lay people. Words that are synonyms in everyday language may be used to describe different products or procedures. Since these irregularities in the use of words often lead to misunderstandings, some terms peculiar to photographic copying and duplication are listed below with their generally accepted meanings.

Characteristic Curve: The graph that shows the relationship between the logarithm of the exposure (in lux seconds) and the resultant density. Also called H&D or D-Log E Curve.

Continuous-Tone Original: An original, such as a photograph, with a continuous range of tones from black to white and many in-between. May be colored or monochrome.

Copy: This term is interchangeable with "original," used most often in the graphic arts industry. Also the photographic print or transparency that is made to replicate the original.

Copy (To Copy): To make copies by photographing two-dimensional, reflective objects, such as photographs, paintings, maps, printed matter, drawings, etc.

Copyboard: An illuminated board, or easel to which the original is attached while being photographed. Copyboards are usually front-lighted, but transparent copyboards may also be lighted from behind for photographing transparent originals.

Copy Negative: The negative obtained by copying or photographing two-dimensional designs, pictures, or documents which are on an opaque base such as paper or canvas.

Copy Print: A positive print made from a copy negative or by copying on a direct positive (reversal) paper.

Copyright: An exclusive right or privilege to publish, reproduce (copy), and distribute one's literary, dramatic, musical, and artistic works, including photographs.

Densitometry: The practice of measuring photographic densities.

Diapositive: Same as an intermediate positive. A film positive made as the intermediate in the production of a duplicate of a film or glass plate negative.

Direct Positive: A positive photographic image that is made on reversal film or paper without the use of an intermediate copy negative. A reversal or direct chemical process may be used.

Document Copying: Photocopying of documents, line drawings, and text materials by electrophotographic or photographic means.

Dupe: Abbreviation for duplicate.

Duplicate: A photographic reproduction of a transparent original, usually a film negative or transparency.

Facsimile: An exact reproduction or copy of the original as far as this is possible within the limitations of the photographic process.

Halftone: A photomechanical reproduction of a continuous-tone original. The continuous tones of the original are represented by tiny dots of pure black and white (or color) called halftone dots.

Intermediate Positive: A film positive made as the intermediate step in the production of a duplicate of a film or glass plate negative — also called a diapositive or interpositive.

Internegative: A negative made from a transparency as the intermediate step in the production of a duplicate transparency or a copy print.

Line Original: An original consisting of "lines" without any intermediate tones. The lines may be alphanumeric (letters or numbers), broad areas of solid tones, colored, black or white on an appropriate background.

Lith: Abbreviation of the word "lithographic." Usually used to describe a film designed for reproducing line or halftone originals, or a developer for producing extremely high contrast.

Magnification: The ratio obtained by dividing image size by the object size. When the ratio is less than one, it is often called the reduction ratio. The ratio multiplied by 100 is the percentage size.

Microfilm: Miniature copies on film of documents, checks, newspapers and such. Retrieval is simplified and storage space much reduced. Particularly suitable for keeping historical material and records, especially when the sheer bulk of paper makes it impossible to store the originals. The microfilm images are commonly 1/5 to 1/50 of the original size.

Original: The design, picture, or document to be copied or duplicated.

Parallelism: The spatial relationship between the film plane and the copyboard. To reproduce a rectangular original as a rectangle, it is essential that the film plane of the camera and the copyboard plane be equidistant at all points.

Photocopy: Generally means a reproduction of a document or drawing made by a photographic or allied process.

Picture: As used in this book, a photograph or artwork representation.

Preservation: Copying or duplicating to preserve the image. The original is not changed.

Radiograph: (Commonly known as an X ray.) An image made on a photographic film or plate by exposure to x rays and from light fluoresced by special screens upon exposure to X rays. The resultant image is a negative.

Reciprocity: The reciprocity law states that exposure equals the illuminance on the emulsion surface times the exposure time. Reciprocity law failure occurs because emulsions change sensitivity with the length of the exposure time or with high or low values of illuminance.

Reflection Copy: Photographic prints, documents, line copy, paintings, and two-dimensional art which are copied by using light that is aimed at their surfaces and which reflects off of the surfaces to the camera.

Registration: The exact physical alignment of two photographic images, often accomplished by the use of pin register systems.

Reproduction: A duplicate of a photograph or similar original.

Restoration: In photography this term usually means to restore a torn, faded, stained, or defaced photograph by a combination of copying, retouching, or other handwork, on a copy negative and/or reproduction print. Technically, however, restoration means treating the original chemically or by some other means to restore it or to improve its condition.

Sensitometry: The science that involves the measurement of the response of photographic emulsions upon exposure to light.

Slide: A transparency made especially for projection. Today most slides are in color and the most common size is 24 x 36 mm contained in 2 x 2-inch mounts.

Sub-surface Illumination: Location of a light source behind the copyboard or easel to provide transmitted light for copying transparent originals. The original is said to be trans-illuminated.

Transparency: A black-and-white or color positive photographic image on a film base which is viewed by transmitted light or projected.

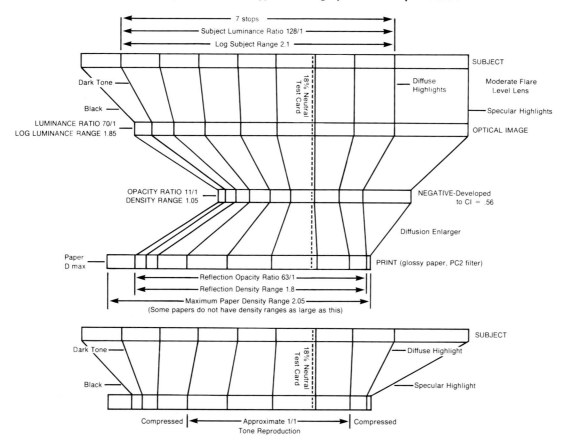

Graphic Representation of Typical Photographic Tone Reproduction

OVERVIEW OF COPYING AND DUPLICATING PROCEDURES

Copying a Photograph

In a simple sense, copying is taking a photograph of a picture. However, if a normal film is used to make the copy negative and a regular process is given the film, the copy print made from the negative will show evidence that it is a copy print—and often may not give satisfactory tone rendition of the original photograph.

This is primarily the result of uneven compression and expansion of tones by photographic film and paper throughout the tonal scale. In the case of electronic imaging, this is less of a problem because of the ability of the computer and appropriate software to change tonal representations. For the unique characteristics of digital photography, see the chapter on digital methods for copying and duplicating.

PHOTOGRAPHIC TONE REPRODUCTION

Photographic films generally compress the dark tones—that is, they show less visual distinction between dark tones than you could see in the original subject. Photographic papers compress both the dark tones and the light tones. Therefore, in a photographic print of an original subject, both the dark tones and the light tones are compressed.

The diagram on page 2 shows how the dark and light tones are compressed. It also shows that the middle tones have been expanded slightly. This type of tone reproduction of an original subject is normal. We are used to seeing this type of tone reproduction in photographs, and we accept it as a reasonably accurate rendition of the original. When we copy a photograph, we start with this type of unevenly compressed tonal rendition. If we take a normal photograph of the original photograph, the dark tones and the light tones get compressed again.

When we look at the copy print, we see dark tones and highlights that have been compressed twice. The diagram on page 4 shows the tone reproduction of a copy print done by normal photographic means. Note that the middles tones have been expanded even more.

To the right, we reproduced an original print, a print from a copy negative on a camera film, and a print from a copy negative on KODAK Professional Copy Film. The compression of the highlight tones in the camera film copy shows up especially in the lighter sky areas.

It is primarily to improve on this type of tone rendition that special copy films are made, and special techniques are used. The last photograph in the series shows a copy print made on a special copy film which gives an improved tone reproduction over that of the normal film.

Reproduction of a print made from the original black-and-white negative. Most of the black-and-white reproductions in this book are printed by the two-black duotone process to maintain as much of the original print quality in the halftone reproductions as possible.

Reproduction of a copy of the upper print made on a general-purpose film. Development was specifically formulated to give the characteristic curve an upsweep, producing a better-quality copy print. Some general-purpose films lose highlight tone separation when used for copying.

Reproduction of a copy of the above print made from a copy negative photographed on KODAK Professional Copy Film. When properly done, the tone-reproduction quality of copy prints made this way can approach that of the original print.

Basic Requirements of a Copy Film

To make the best possible copy photograph, some method of reducing the compression in the highlights is required, and, at the same time, a method of reducing the mid-tone expansion is usually needed.

There are two photographic materials used in making a copy, the negative film and the paper. The tone reproduction characteristics of the paper are relatively fixed. The paper must go from white to black—all the way through the tonal range. Because of this requirement, there is no way to eliminate the shoulder and toe from a paper characteristic curve. It is the paper curve toe that compresses the highlight tones and the shoulder that compresses the shadow tones. Since the paper cannot be used to improve the tone reproduction of the copy, it is the film that must do the job.

Kodak has designed a black-and-white film especially for copying that has an unusual characteristic curve. The portion of the curve used to record the dark and middle tones has a normal slope. The portion of the curve used to record the light tones has an upward sweep with a higher degree of contrast. A copy negative, properly exposed, records the dark and middle tones with normal contrast but records the light tones with higher contrast. This expands the light tones that were previously compressed by the original film and paper. Kodak color copy films are available with the same characteristics. An ideal copy film would also expand the shadow tones. However, this is not possible photographically, because shadow detail must be recorded at the time of exposure.

Graphic Representation of Copy Tone Reproductions

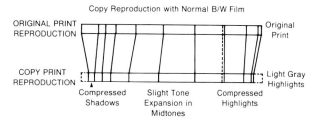

The drawing shows the severe highlight tone compression in a copy print made using a regular camera film as a copy film. The lower drawing shows the improvement in highlight tone reproduction achieved by using KODAK Professional Copy Film.

Special Copy Films That Improve Tone Reproduction

KODAK Professional Copy Film 4125 (ESTAR Thick Base) is the black-and-white sheet film especially designed for copying. The curves of this film on the next page show how the basic contrast of the dark and midtone range is slightly adjustable by changing the amount of development. In practice, once a satisfactory developing time has been determined, this time is used for each copy negative, while the negative contrast is controlled by increasing or decreasing the amount of exposure.

The lower left drawing shows two exposures on a copy film characteristic curve. The log exposure range is the same for each exposure. The upper exposure is 1 stop more than the first.

The density range of the negative resulting from the 14-second exposure is 1.05, while the 28-second negative has a density range of 1.25. Note that in the second exposure, much more of the lighter portion of the original has been exposed on the upsweep part of the curve—hence the medium-light tones have been expanded in addition to the normal expansion of the light tones. The 14-second exposure is the better one.

There are three Kodak color films that have similar characteristic curves to that of KODAK Professional Copy Film. The first is KODAK VERICOLOR Internegative Film 4112 (ESTAR Thick Base) in sheet form. The second and third are KODAK Commercial Internegative Film 4325 in sheets and 5325 in rolls, made especially for copying transparencies. The illustrations show the characteristic curves of these films. The particular uses of these films are discussed later in this publication.

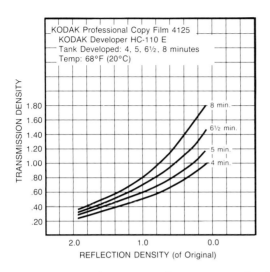

Characteristic curves of KODAK Professional Copy Film developed for different times. Five minutes is the recommended time for tank development in KODAK HC-110 Developer, Dilution E.

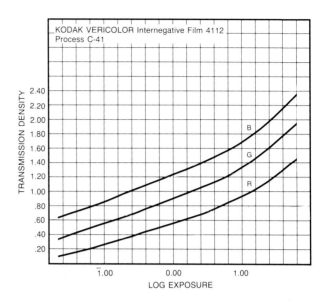

Characteristic curves of KODAK VERICOLOR Internegative Film 4112, showing the upsweep in the curves designed to enhance highlight tone separation when copying either color prints or transparencies. Negative density range (density difference) is controlled entirely by exposure.

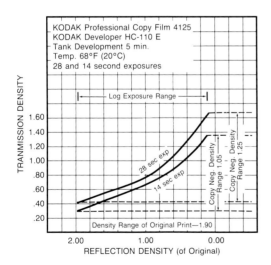

Characteristic curves of KODAK Professional Copy Film showing how contrast as measured by negative density range is controlled primarily by changing the copy exposure.

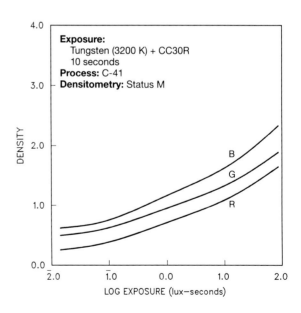

KODAK Commercial Internegative Film 4325/5325 is designed specifically for making color negatives from transparencies. The color sensitivity of each of the layers is designed to permit the interchangeable copying of transparencies made on KODACHROME and EKTACHROME Films.

COPYRIGHT AND RESTRICTIONS

Before you reproduce (copy or duplicate) a photograph or a transparency, it is advisable to determine who owns the rights to reproduce that photograph or transparency. For instance, a person may purchase the rights to use photographs or transparencies, but the right to reproduce such photographs or transparencies is often retained by the original photographer unless an agreement has been drawn up between the photographer and the person purchasing these images.

Copyright

The Copyright Act is a federal law enacted by Congress providing a form of monopoly for a limited time to encourage the production and publication of literary, dramatic, musical, and artistic works. The Copyright Act grants the owner of a copyright certain exclusive rights, including the right to publish and reproduce the copyrighted work and the right to distribute copies to the public by sale, rental, lease, or lending. Certain works, for example those for which the statutory monopoly period has expired, are in the public domain and may be freely copied. However, to avoid potential copyright problems, it is always safer, as well as more courteous, to get written permission from the owner or the photographer, as the case may be, before copying a photograph or transparency.

Restrictions

OFFICIAL DOCUMENTS
Federal law forbids the copying of United States and foreign government obligations, such as paper currency (paper money), treasury notes, bonds, bills, checks, drafts, and similar papers. Also, it is unlawful to copy postage stamps, internal revenue stamps—see below for philatelic exceptions— passports, drivers' licenses, immigration papers, U.S. government identification cards, badges, or insignia, as well as military records or documents labeled "secret," "top secret," "confidential," or "restricted."

EXCEPTIONS TO COPYING REGULATIONS
U.S. postage stamps and coins generally may be copied for identification or publication purposes. U.S. stamps, however, have the following copying restrictions: the reproductions must be in black and white only, and less than 3/4 or more than 1 1/2 times the size of the stamp.

CAUTIONARY NOTE
The foregoing brief commentary of conditions relating to photographic copying is for informational purposes only. It is not intended to be legal advice and the publisher assumes no responsibility for actions based on the above statements. If you are unfamiliar with the law pertaining to copyright or have any doubt about the legality of copying anything, obtain legal advice before proceeding.

For general information regarding federal copyright law and procedures, write to the following address:

Registrar of Copyrights
Library of Congress
Washington, D.C. 20559

EQUIPMENT

Photographic copying requires the use of equipment that is basically similar to the equipment required for duplicating. Therefore, equipment will be considered first, and then its use in copying and in duplicating will be discussed.

Basic Requirements

A camera of some kind, a copyboard or easel, and light for illumination of the original and exposure of the photographic film or paper are the essential elements of any copying and duplicating equipment. There are at least four typical arrangements of these elements shown in the illustration.

Probably the most important requirements for any equipment include the following.

(1) **The camera must be mounted so that the lens axis is in line and perpendicular with the center of the copyboard.** This will help having the image centered in the image plane of the camera. Copyboards often have areas outlined with markings of some kind to aid in centering an original on the copyboard. This can be readily accomplished by drawing rectangles the size of the standard photographic paper sizes — 4 x 5, 5 x 7, 8 x 10, 10 x 12, 14 x 17 inches — having the center of the rectangles coinciding with the center of the copyboard and therefore, the lens axis.

(2) **The copyboard and film plane must be parallel to each other to avoid image distortion.** In addition, depth of field is shallow when lenses are close focused, and portions of the copy may be out of focus if the film plane and copyboard are not absolutely parallel. This can be accomplished by using a spirit level on both the vertical and horizontal sides of the copyboard and the camera. Some commercial equipment has spirit levels mounted in both directions. This procedure may not be considered precise enough in certain situations. A better technique is to have an accurate grid pattern on the focusing screen of the camera and then adjust either the copyboard or the camera, or both, until the grid pattern shows no distortion—vertically or horizontally.

A. Top view of a horizontal arrangement for copying prints.
B. Top view of a horizontal arrangement for copying transparencies.
C. Front view of a vertical arrangement for copying prints.
D. Front view of a vertical arrangement for copying transparencies.

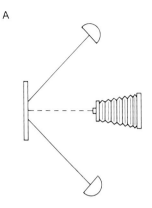

A

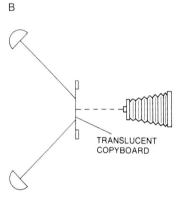

B

TRANSLUCENT
COPYBOARD

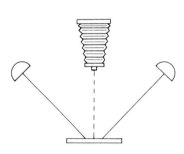

C

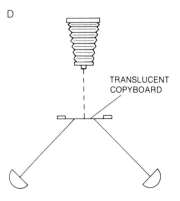

D

TRANSLUCENT
COPYBOARD

7

Once the image of the copyboard center is centered on the ground glass, the perpendicularity of the copyboard to the lens axis can be checked with a flat mirror. A mirror is placed on the center of the copyboard, and the image of the camera lens will then be seen on the ground glass. If the image of the lens reflection is not centered on the ground glass, the copyboard is not perpendicular with the axis. Adjust the copyboard until the image of the lens is centered on the ground glass; it is then perpendicular to the axis.

A much-refined version of these techniques is used when large master drawings are reduced 100X or more to produce master negatives for use in reticle or microcircuitry production. In some of these applications a traveling microscope mounted on a camera back is used to ensure parallelism and dimensional accuracy within 1/10,000 of an inch or better.

(3) **The lights used to illuminate the copyboard should be mounted to permit adjustment both vertically and horizontally.** In general, copy lights are arranged so that they are on the same axis as the lens. (See copyboard illumination on page 27.)

(4) **A ground-glass focusing screen is recommended.** Most large-format cameras are equipped with a ground-glass screen that rests in the film plane for accurate focusing. If one is not available, a piece of ground glass can be placed across the back in the film plane. The camera is then focused and the glass is removed so a film back can be put into position for the exposure.

Among 35mm and medium-format cameras, the design of choice is the single-lens-reflex since it permits the viewing of the ground glass through the viewfinder without having to remove and replace the film each time. But a note of caution here—SLR designs vary in terms of how much of the actual picture area is recorded on film versus what is shown on the ground glass. The Pentax 6x7 Camera, for example, displays only about 90% in its viewfinder (true with prism finders; the waist-level folding finder and rigid magnifying finder both yield 100% images), and the result may be a final composition that includes unwanted material around the periphery of the framing. It is generally a good idea to check the camera's specifications, see what percentage the viewfinder shows of the total recorded picture, and frame accordingly.

Rangefinder and twin-lens cameras can also be used for copy work, but these must first be prefocused using a piece of ground glass or acetate across the film plane. Then the film is loaded into the camera which precludes any accurate refocusing for a new composition until the roll is finished, all of which is not a very practical arrangement.

Another consideration with 35mm SLR cameras is the use of AF (autofocus) modes. Again, this function varies according to the camera maker, and even models within a product line might be slightly different in performance such that it may not be possible to use the AF function when copying. Part of this may be due to the nature of the subject matter, since AF systems characteristically need a defined pattern on which to lock their focus. Fortunately, virtually all of the modern SLR AF cameras have a provision for switching to manual focus.

These four requirements provide the basis upon which practically all copying and duplicating equipment is designed. Anything else is a matter of refinement, for example, greater precision, multiple lamps for illumination, vacuum frames to hold original copy in place, camera backs that accept long rolls of film, bellows and extension tubes to permit focusing for close-up pictures, filter-pack holders, automatic exposure control, and others.

The range of equipment varies from simple adaptations of amateur and view cameras to elaborate graphic arts cameras called process cameras, to precise instruments for microfilming in quantity and for the production of printed circuit boards. The primary consideration here is with equipment for copying and duplicating flat originals where the end product is a photographic reproduction.

The best choice of equipment for any particular reproduction work is difficult to make without knowledge of all the circumstances, but the following considerations form a broad basis for making the choice.

(1) If a few copy negatives are needed only occasionally, a homemade stand, such as that illustrated by the drawing on the top of page 9, together with a view camera will serve the purpose.

(2) If the maximum size of the originals and the negatives required from them are both large, the installation will occupy a considerable amount of floor space. Process, or graphic arts, camera-and-copyboard units are suitable for such applications. See description on page 15.

(3) If space is limited, consider a vertical copy camera, rather than the horizontal type.

(4) High-volume copying of small originals is routine work in photofinishing plants. Speed of operation is a main feature of equipment for this purpose. Consider exposing and processing material in long rolls for speed in handling.

(5) If the copying work is varied, look for the versatility of the equipment.

Simple Equipment

When expensive commercial equipment is not justified or available, there are setups that can be built or assembled. An image to be copied can be attached to a wall or other solid, flat, vertical surface. A camera mounted on a tripod is set up so the center of the image coincides with the lens axis. Use a spirit level and careful measurement to be sure the original and film plane of the camera are parallel to avoid image distortion. Two or four studio flood lamps can be used for illumination.

A more permanent horizontal setup can be built having the copyboard, the camera, and the lights mounted on a common base. The camera can be mounted on a box of sufficient height that the center of the copyboard coincides with the lens axis and in such a manner that the box moves backwards and forwards between two rails at right angles to the copyboard. (See illustration.)

A horizontal slide-copying device can be made consisting of a single-lens-reflex camera, bellows focusing attachment, homemade bracket, diffuser, electronic flash unit, and rubber bands to hold the original slide and filters in position. The diffuser, required to scatter the light, can be translucent glass or translucent acrylic plastic such as DuPont Lucite® Type 4447 or 2447 Plexiglas. The horizontal track supporting the equipment parts is made extra long so that the unit can also be used for copying type, artwork, photos, and other flat-plane subjects that are larger than 35mm slides. (See illustrations.)

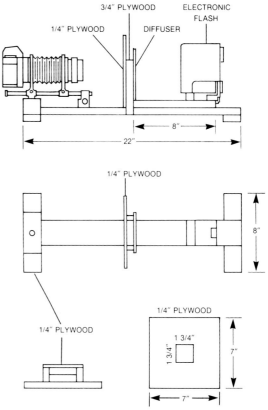

Horizontal Slide-Copy Stand
With a minimum of hardware, a few plywood scraps, and a diffusing sheet, you can construct your own slide-copying device. Purchase a one-inch bolt (1/4"-20), nut, and washer at your local hardware store to secure your camera/bellows/lens to the frame. For a diffuser you can use a piece of translucent glass or plastic, cut to fit. To cut out the square opening in the vertical easel, use a saber or keyhole saw. Adjust all of your vertical measurements to match the heights of your own bellows attachment and electronic flash.

The horizontal track supporting the slide/diffuser/flash assembly is extra long so that the unit can also be used for copying type, artwork, photos, and other flat-plane subjects that are larger than 35mm slides.

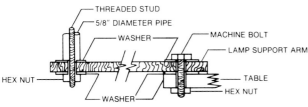

Adjustable Light Support Arm

Schematic drawing of a convenient horizontal copy stand. The copyboard is movable to change image size. The camera is usually left stationary to make it convenient to view the ground glass from the end of the bench, although it can also be moved. Dimensions are flexible to fit particular needs.

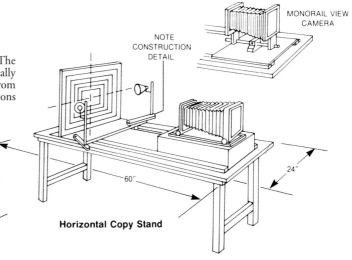

Horizontal Copy Stand

Commercially Available Equipment

Photographic Enlargers: Some enlargers are designed so they can be converted for use as a camera in vertical copying and duplicating. This entails removing the lamphouse and substituting a camera back for the negative carrier. Lights to illuminate the original are attached either to the column or the baseboard.

This approach could be useful in very small photolabs where equipment must be reduced to a minimum or for amateurs who do their own laboratory work. Of course, such an enlarger could also be converted to a permanent setup.

35MM EQUIPMENT AND ACCESSORIES

Many copying and duplication jobs can be accomplished using a 35mm camera. Copy stands for use with those cameras are available from camera stores and photographic equipment suppliers. These stands usually consist of an upright column mounted on a baseboard.

The camera is attached to the column by means of its tripod socket and an arm-and-collar assembly, which slides up and down the column. Two or four lights to illuminate the original are also mounted on the column at a suitable distance from the baseboard. Some of these stands can be disassembled and carried in a case when copying must be done on location, as might be necessary when working in a museum or an art gallery.

The 35mm single-lens-reflex is by far the most suitable camera for use on a copy stand, because the image is clearly visible for focusing and centering the original on the film. Another advantage of the SLR is the ability to preview the depth of field at smaller apertures. Some SLRs have a simple attachment available that permits reversing the lens position for better resolution when very-close focusing is required.

Special finder attachments are made for some 35mm single-lens-reflex cameras that permit viewing at right angles to the camera. These can be especially useful in some copying situations. Reflex finders also prevent light coming through the finder eye lens from reaching the photocells, thus helping to avoid false exposure measurements. This is illustrated on page 12.

It is very difficult to frame the image exactly on the film with rangefinder cameras because the camera lens and the viewfinder lens do not have the same field of view in close-up work. This condition is called parallax. However, the image can be focused and centered by opening the camera back and placing a small piece of fine ground glass or matte acetate in the position normally occupied by the film. The ground side of the glass must face the camera lens in order to be located in the focal plane. Then the shutter is set for a time exposure (T) or bulb (B) and triggered so that it remains open. To make the image more visible, darken the room or use a dark focusing cloth.

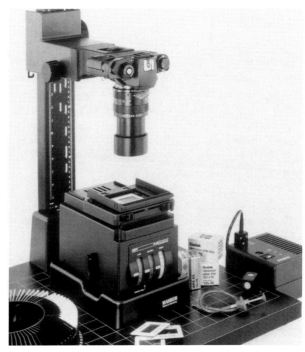

A small copy stand is useful with 35mm cameras for making copies from originals of a limited size. With the addition of an illuminator, the copy stand can be used to make transparency duplicates and copy negatives of transparencies.

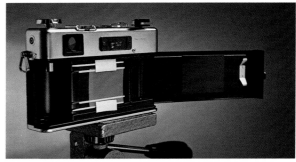

A ground glass or piece of sheet acetate can be used for framing the image of copies with a 35mm camera that does not have a reflex finder.

Extension tubes (left) or a focusing bellows can be used with single-lens-reflex cameras for extending the lens-to-film distance for close-focusing.

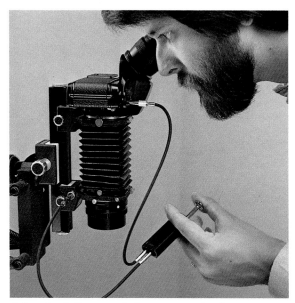

A focusing bellows attached to a camera in place on a copy stand. The original can usually be magnified several times on the film at maximum bellows extension.

Greater cropping flexibility is provided by this more-sophisticated bellows duplicating equipment.

Four methods of close-focusing for copying and duplicating are represented by these lenses. On the left is a non-focusing lens for use with a bellows attachment. Top center is a macro lens which has extra-long focusing threads. Macro lenses usually give up to a magnification of 0.5X (half-size) to 1.0X (full-size) on the film without other attachments. On the right is a lens with a lens-reversing ring. Regular camera lenses usually give sharper images at extremely close distances when placed "backwards" on the camera. At the bottom are close-up lenses which are attached to the camera lens like filters for close-focusing.

Accessories for 35mm Cameras: The standard focal length of a lens for a 35mm camera is about 50mm. Usually these lenses have a minimum focusing distance of about 2 feet. As a practical matter, this means that the largest image of an 8 x 10-inch original, for example, is just about large enough to fill the negative.

For shorter distances than the 2 feet normally available, focusing cannot be done by the camera focusing mechanism. There are several methods by which a lens on an SLR camera can be made to focus closer. The most practical for copy work are to increase the lens-to-film plane distance as with the use of an extension ring (extension tube) or bellows placed between the lens and the camera, or to place a high-quality close-up lens (diopter) on the front of the lens. Both will result in being able to focus closer to the subject and that will increase the on-film magnification of the subject.

Of the two methods, the lens extension arrangement usually yields better results since you are not introducing another lens element, as is being done with the close-up lens. Also, the extension methods provide for a much greater range and a higher degree of on-film magnification up to and well beyond 1:1 or "life-size" magnifications. On the other hand, the use of a diopter-type close-up arrangement does not result in the need for an increase in exposure as does any arrangement where the lens-to-film distance is increased. If a diopter is to be used, it is highly recommended that the multi-element type as manufactured by such camera companies as Nikon, Canon, and Leica be used, as opposed to the more commonly available single-element types.

Diopters (which are also called supplementary lenses and close-up filters) are usually rated as +1, +2, +3, etc., with greater magnification the result of using higher numbers. They also can be doubled up in which case the power is additive. That is, +1 and +2 on the same lens is the equivalent of a +3 lens. There is some disagreement about which close-up lens to put on the camera first, though the most common practice is to install the most powerful lens first.

In any case, single-element close-up lens designs are not recommended for critical copy work. Very good results are obtainable with the more expensive multi-element-type close-up lenses, but it is also not recommended that these be stacked for greater magnification when working for the best-quality results. If greater on-film magnification is required, use the extension method, preferably in conjunction with a macro lens.

A waist-level finder attachment mounted on a single-lens-reflex camera permits easier framing and focusing when doing vertical copying or duplicating.

A magnifying, angled viewfinder gives an enlarged view of the image at an easy-to-use viewing angle.

A rotating viewfinder is yet another type of accessory that makes copying and duplicating easier.

To make a life-size copy (1:1 magnification) requires the image and the object to be copied each to be two focal lengths from the lens. A 2X magnification would have the size of the image in the film plane twice as large as the original object.

With a 35mm camera equipped with a 50mm lens, the distance between the lens and film plane must be extended to achieve 1:1 or greater magnification. As indicated before, this can be done by using either a bellows focusing attachment or a set of extension rings between the lens and the camera. (See illustration on page 10.) Most bellows devices will extend a normal lens to a distance great enough to produce focused images at a 3X or larger magnification. Both bellows

focusing attachments and extension tubes reduce the amount of light reaching the film in proportion to their length, and it is necessary to correct the exposure according to the instructions that come with the equipment. The effect of magnification on exposure is discussed on page 34. At these distances, the lens should be reversed to obtain better sharpness.

In the case of 35mm slide duplication, specially designed units are commercially available. Both types of close-focusing devices provide 1:1 magnification when used with an SLR camera equipped with a normal 50-55mm lens. The illustration shows the adaptation of both the bellows focusing and the extension tube accessories. These commercial units also have a built-in light source, filter drawer, and diffusion panel. Some also have dichroic filters to control the color balance.

In any case, the light source should be consistent in color balance. Electronic flash, which is daylight-balanced, is consistent and also allows the use of a small *f*-number for greater depth of field, although some correction may be needed with automatic flash at close distances (due to reciprocity failure at the ensuing extremely short flash durations; use in manual mode for slide-duping applications). Photoflood lamps, balanced for Type A film, can be used but require longer exposures and may result in poor exposures due to reciprocity failure of films not designed for long exposure times (see glossary for definition of reciprocity).

Macro lenses, which have long focusing threads, permit close-focusing. When used alone the largest image produced is from about 1/2 life-size to life-size, depending on the particular lens. When used in combination with extension tubes or bellows the range can be extended to reproduce subjects two, three, or more times larger than life-size on the film. Macro lenses have excellent optical performance at close distances and are easy to use. They are available in normal to moderate telephoto focal lengths and focus smoothly from infinity to just a few inches in front of the lens. There are also some zoom macro lenses available but the sharpness of copy negatives may not be as good as with single focal length lenses, pin cushion distortion may occur, and most do not approach 1:1 magnification. Most macro lenses are made for 35mm cameras and a few for cameras that use 120 film. Process lenses, special copy lenses, and macro lenses are also made for sheet film cameras.

Many 35mm cameras have interchangeable viewfinders and/or focusing screens. Some auxiliary viewfinders that are useful in copying are illustrated.

The finder shown in the second picture is used with the pentaprism removed. It is a waist-level viewfinder that has a flip-up magnifier. This is useful when the camera is used on a copy stand at eye level. Because a pentaprism is not used, the image is reversed from left to right. This is the simplest and least expensive type of auxiliary viewfinder.

The other two viewfinders must be mounted in a special pentaprism that is made for certain auxiliary viewfinders. The third illustration shows a magnification viewfinder. It enlarges the image of the frame and aids in critical focusing. The last type of viewfinder can be rotated to either the right angle position or to the normal position. Because it is used with a pentaprism, the image is oriented correctly from left to right.

Interchangeable focusing screens may be helpful for improving ease of focusing with certain specialized types of screens at high magnifications. Other screens are available with ruled lines that are useful when trying to square up a copy image in the camera. In the case of many focusing screens and especially those commonly used in SLR designs, a frequent problem is "screen blackout." This occurs in low-light conditions with focusing screens that have microprism center circles for critical focus or split-image center circles. Here, part or all of the critical center focusing circle will go black and cannot be used. In these cases, just use thc ground glass portion around the circle to focus.

Vertical Camera Equipment

Vertical Copy Stands: In addition to the small copy stands described earlier for use with 35mm cameras, more elaborate stands can be obtained that can be used with almost any size camera including 35mm. Long-roll backs are available for many 35mm and 2 1/4 x 2 1/4 professional cameras. Although conventional picture-taking cameras are not necessarily the best for copying and duplicating, most can be of good service when it is not financially feasible or desirable to buy a special copy camera. The nature and volume of the copying work dictates the best kind of equipment to use. Cameras which permit ground glass focusing make framing and focusing much faster and more accurate.

A complete copy stand with lights for 35mm vertical copying. Fairly large originals can be copied with this equipment.

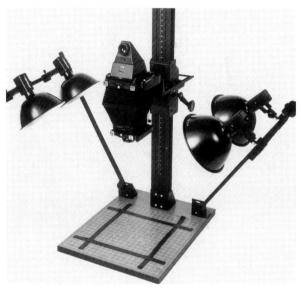

Larger copy stands are required for vertical copying with view cameras. Note the accessory finder that permits easy magnified viewing of the ground-glass image.

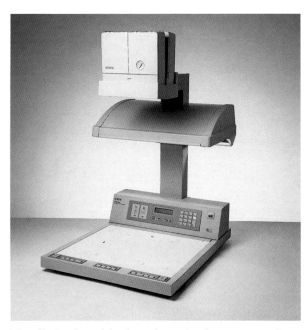

Microfilming bound books and oversize documents requires a sophisticated flatbed machine or vertical copier such as the KODAK IMAGELINK Planetary Microimager.

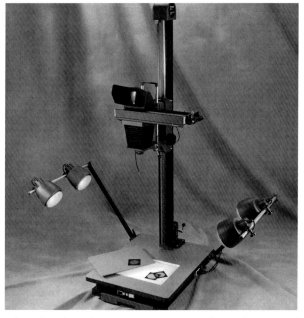

The Polaroid MP 4+ Camera System is a professional copy stand which features eye-level reflex viewing and a camera head that rotates 360° with an optional rotating support column. Interchangeable film holders allow the use of Polaroid pack and sheet films and pre-loaded film packets, such as KODAK READYLOAD packets.

Vertical Copy Cameras for General Work: If your copying and duplicating work is considerable in volume and if it is of a general nature, including originals up to 20 x 24 inches, consider a vertical copy camera similar to the ones shown here and on page 14.

Vertical cameras are generally easy to operate but should be equipped with a reflex hood or other device to facilitate sizing and correct placement of the image on the film. Interchangeable camera backs allow various sizes of film to be used, and roll-film backs enable quantities of copy negatives to be processed continuously.

A vertical camera occupies less floor space than a horizontal model with the same capability. Some vertical cameras are constructed with high vertical columns and often require more head room than most other units.

Specialized Equipment for Microfilming: Microfilming is essentially a photographic document copying operation to produce reduced images on film of documents of all kinds and sizes. The objectives of microfilming include: (1) the reduction of storage space; (2) a more readily accessible file; (3) security of valuable records often by storage of a duplicate in a safe and environmentally controlled location; and (4) use of the negative to produce a smaller size print of the original for field use as with large engineering drawings.

Microfilming bound books and oversize documents requires a sophisticated flatbed machine or vertical copier such as the KODAK IMAGELINK Planetary Microimager. This unit features automatic exposure control to adjust for variations in document types and size sensors in the copyboard to automatically determine the proper reduction factor. A zoom lens makes the necessary adjustment in less than a second. A precise film-management system monitors usage to help get the maximum number of images per roll of microfilm. A foot switch permits the operator to place and film documents continuously in a hands-off fashion.

Originals up to 11 x 17 inches (279 mm x 432 mm or A3) can be photographed. The reduction range is 25:1 and 32:1. Additionally, the KODAK IMAGELINK Planetary Microimager integrates with most computer-assisted retrieval systems, allowing users to combine the benefits of microfilm and digital imaging.

Scanner-microimagers, such as the KODAK IMAGELINK Scanner/Microimager 990, capture image information in digital form and on film in a single pass. Indexing is also performed automatically during the capture stage. In this scenario, microfilm images are stored off-line for long-term retention. Digital images are stored on short-term magnetic media.

The digital image and the document index number are both stored in the database. The digital image can be erased after a predetermined period. The index is retained, so the document image can be retrieved from microfilm in the future.

This kind of integration within electronic systems is enabling microfilm to offer retrieval speeds that are far faster than those of the past. Today, some microfilm retrieval systems can deliver an image to a desktop computer in three minutes. Future enhancements will allow even faster delivery.

Microfilm access time will never match on-line or near-line digital storage. But it will make microfilm a very attractive complement to digital storage, offering users unique advantages in terms of cost and assurance of access.

Complete information about Kodak products and solutions for document management can be obtained by writing to Eastman Kodak Company, Business Imaging Systems, 901 Elmgrove Road, Rochester, New York 14653 or by visiting the Kodak home page on the World Wide Web at http://www.kodak.com.

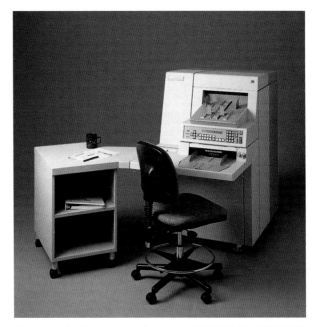

Scanner-microimagers, such as the KODAK IMAGELINK Scanner/Microimager 990, capture image information in digital form and on film in a single pass.

Horizontal Camera Equipment

Horizontal Process Cameras: There are several makes of large horizontal cameras or process cameras like those used in the graphic arts. The copyboard assembly travels on rails that may extend for 12 feet or more. The whole outfit, including the darkroom, often occupies a space of about 12 x 24 feet. The equipment is usually arranged so that the camera back can be fitted into an opening in the wall of a small darkroom. Thus, sizing, focusing, and placing the image on the ground glass are done by remote control adjacent to the camera back within the darkroom. The copyboard usually consists of a board covered with a glass frame to hold the copy flat. For special jobs a vacuum copyboard is often used, and some copyboards are designed to permit illumination of a transparency original from behind. Even though you may intend to use the equipment primarily for black-and-white work, it is important to make sure that the illumination is of a suitable type and balance for color work for the few jobs that may be done in color.

Not all process cameras are fitted to a darkroom. Some may be precision cameras that can be set up for both large and small originals. They may have a camera back designed for use with regular sheet film holders.

Vertical Process Cameras: There are also some vertical process cameras of this type available that are very useful in limited-space darkrooms. These are all rigid, precision, versatile setups that can be used to copy originals of practically any size but have a limited magnification range.

Lenses For Copying And Duplicating

Basic Requirements: A photographic lens can be designed to focus sharply across a flat plane at only one object distance. Most lenses for general work are designed to have a flat field at object distances greater than 8X the focal length. Most copying is done at close distances, and at close distances the sharp image field of such lenses is curved. This makes it difficult to obtain copy images that are sharp simultaneously both in the center and at the edges.

One way of compensating for this effect is to increase the depth of field by stopping the lens down to very small apertures (very large *f*-numbers). While this helps in most instances, it has several drawbacks. First, very small apertures introduce a high degree of diffraction which reduces the sharpness of the image. Second, it lengthens the exposure time. Not only does this require more time, it also frequently places exposure times where reciprocity-law failure becomes a sizable factor. With very long exposure times, the contrast of a negative copy film image is likely to change, requiring a change in development. In color films, long exposure times not only require a further adjustment in exposure, but usually also require filtration to help compensate for color shifts. Long exposure times also increase the possibility of sharpness loss due to equipment vibration.

The best optics to use for copy work in the case of 35mm and medium-format cameras are macro lenses. These lenses have been engineered for close-focusing situations, and some of the longer focal lengths are made with low-dispersion glass and offer correction of chromatic aberration. Process lenses have been available for large-format cameras with their characteristically flat fields, and there are now also several macro formulas as well.

Another optical requirement is that the lenses used should produce *even* illumination across the focal plane. Critical examination of negatives reveals that most will be found more dense in the center than at the edges. This is due to the greater intensity of light at the center than at the perimeter of the circle of illumination projected by the lens. Wide-angle lenses for large formats have serious illumination falloff. This may not be too serious in the copying of continuous-tone originals on relatively low contrast films but the effect is normally accentuated to a serious degree on high-contrast negatives of line originals. This effect can be minimized by stopping the lens down and by using one that has a focal length slightly longer than normal for the film size being used. Some improvement can also be achieved by control of the copyboard illumination. See "Lighting" on page 26.

A process lens. Because such lenses are always used at close-working distances, equivalent *f*-numbers are marked for different percent sizes (magnifications). Most modern copy lenses are multicoated, which lowers the flare level.

Most process lenses available today are apochromatic lenses, that is, they are designed for better correction of chromatic aberrations. They are corrected so that images formed by light of three specific different colors all focus sharply in the same plane, which means that they are corrected for longitudinal chromatic aberration. They are also corrected for the difference in magnification of images in different colors—an aberration called lateral chromatic aberration which causes colored fringes at the edges of an image. Apochromatic lenses *must* be used for critical work in color copying and duplicating, and, of course, they perform well with any kind of original.

The correct focal length lens for use in copying and duplicating depends largely on the size of the negative to be covered with acceptable sharpness. As a general rule, the focal length should be at least equal to the diagonal measurement of the negative format. The table below can be a useful guide.

Negative Diagonals

Size of Negative	Diagonal Measurement in Inches (approx.)	Diagonal Measurement in Millimetres (approx.)
35 mm	1³/₄	45
4.5 x 6 cm	3	75
2¹/₄ x 2¹/₄ in	3¹/₄	80
6 x 7 cm	3⁵/₈	92
2¹/₄ x 3¹/₄ in.	4	100
4 x 5 in.	6¹/₄	160
5 x 7 in.	8¹/₂	220
8 x 10 in.	12³/₄	325
11 x 14 in.	18	455

Copyboards

A copyboard is essentially a flat, firm surface to which the original can be attached for copying. The board is illuminated with an arrangement of lights. The important features are that the board should be perfectly parallel to the camera back or focal plane, and be vibration free. Lack of parallelism results in a distorted image, making it difficult to get all of the subject focused sharply, and, of course, vibrations cause unsharp negatives.

A simple copyboard can be made by attaching a sheet of soft wood, cork, or cardboard-type building board to a wall, or other firm support. The board should be painted matte black to minimize flare and reflections. A white copyboard maximizes flare, a gray copyboard gives moderate flare, while a black copyboard minimizes flare. The same applies to any flat work mounted in a white or very light frame. If the frame is not to be recorded in the photograph, it should be covered with a matte black covering. Flare causes a loss in contrast, extra compression of shadow tones, and lowers definition somewhat. It is useful to have concentric outlines of the most common paper sizes printed on the copyboard to aid in centering the originals on the copyboard.

Holding the Original in Place: Originals can be held down by pushpins, but it is not always desirable, or permissible, to make pinholes in the edges of a picture or a document. Alternatives are to use a steel copyboard and to hold the original with small bar magnets, or to hang a printing frame on the copyboard and put the original in that. Some manufactured copyboards have four jointed, spring-steel "fingers" to hold the four corners of the copy.

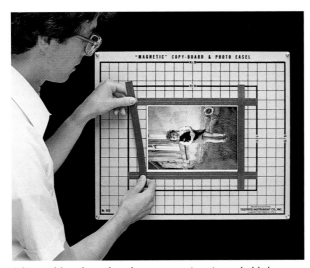

This steel-based copyboard uses magnetic strips to hold the copy flat. The lines on the copyboard aid in orienting and centering the copy. Such a copyboard is quite suitable for the horizontal copy stand shown on page 9.

In copying with a vertical camera, holding the original in place is simplified. If the copy is free from curl, or quite flat, nothing is needed to hold it down. If the original does not lie flat, hold it down with a piece of optically clear, colorless glass, which is clean and free from defects.

Many professional-type cameras are equipped with copyboards that can be rotated for easy copy orientation of the originals. A hinged glass frame clamps the copy to the board. The whole assembly is then rotated to the vertical position for focusing and exposing.

Vacuum Copyboards: Basically, a vacuum copyboard or easel consists of a board perforated by many small holes. A vacuum pump sucks air through these holes and the resulting suction holds the original in place. Boards of this kind are used in process cameras to hold the film in place. (In making big enlargements similar boards are used for holding up big sheets of enlarging paper.)

The principal use for vacuum copyboards is for holding very large and flimsy originals, such as maps or engineering drawings. A great deal of time is saved by avoiding awkward manipulation of the material. A vacuum board and the pump that creates the suction are relatively expensive, but the cost is justified by a saving in time when the work is of sufficient volume or when precision copying is required. Tank-type, "wet/dry" vacuum cleaners can be used as a source of vacuum for smaller-sized, homemade vacuum copyboards.

Light Sources For Copyboard Illumination

Any source of light—including daylight—can be used for copying and duplicating on black-and-white films. Some black-and-white films may have slightly different sensitivities to electronic flash and daylight versus tungsten light, and this becomes evident when filters are used. For example, when using KODAK T-MAX 100 Professional Film, the filter factor for the blue 47 filter is 8 for daylight or electronic flash and 25 for tungsten. When copying with color films, the color temperature of the copyboard illumination must match that for which the film is designed.

Incandescent: Ordinary tungsten studio lamps (3200 K) are suitable for most applications, including color (when used with tungsten-balanced film). For small setups reflector-type bulbs can be used, but since the built-in reflector does not always mask the light, a lens hood should be used on the copy camera lens to reduce flare.

Photofloods (3400 K) can also be used for most copying, but due to their relatively short life they are not as economical as ordinary tungsten studio lamps.

Light Sources Used in Copying

Light Source	Color Temperature	Color Film Type	KODAK Light Balancing Filter
Tungsten Studio Lamp	3200 K	Tungsten (Type B)	No Filter
Photofloods	3400 K	Tungsten (Type A)	No Filter
		Tungsten (Type B)	81A
Blue Photofloods	4800 K	Daylight	82B
Quartz-Iodine (Tungsten-Halogen)	3200 K	Tungsten (Type B)	No Filter
100W General Service Incandescent	2900 K	Tungsten (Type B)	82B
Pulsed Xenon†	6000 K	Daylight	81A*
Electronic Flash	5600 - 6500 K	Daylight	81, 81A, 81B*

*Some light sources balanced for daylight may give an accurate color rendition on daylight balanced film without filtration.
†Not recommended for color. See text.

Note: Color copying with regular fluorescent light sources is not recommended because of the difficulties obtaining accurate color correction.

Safety Note: It is recommended that the manufacturer of the pulsed-xenon or quartz-iodine (tungsten-halogen) lamps be consulted for safety information pertaining to ultraviolet radiation and ventilation requirements due to ozone generation.

A reflector-flood lamp is shown at left. A tungsten bulb suitable for use in a reflector is at right. Above is an electronic flash unit suitable for copy work.

Electronic Flash: Electronic flash is balanced for daylight (5500 K) and should be used with daylight-type color films. Filtration may be required for exact color balance. Pulsed-xenon lights are essentially daylight balance but are usually not recommended for color because color contrast shifts may occur which cannot be corrected with filters.

There are several advantages to using electronic flash as a light source. Flash duration is very short, preventing camera shake from introducing blur into the copy or duplicate. Also, color balance is very consistent provided the capacitor is always fully charged when shooting. The color temperature of the light that is emitted from electronic flash tubes is much more consistent than most tungsten sources. Electronic flash may still require filtration to achieve good color balance. An 81B filter often provides good color balance. Electronic flash is a cool light source. Unlike tungsten light sources, electronic flash does not generate much heat. Modeling lamps, which are tungsten lamps used in conjunction with electronic flash tubes to provide light for focusing, are generally low wattage and so do not generate excessive heat. However, modeling lights should be turned off during the exposure to avoid possible mixed balance illumination.

There are two disadvantages to using electronic flash. The first disadvantage is that exposure determination often must be accomplished with a test. Flash meters are a good way to determine exposure. For some duplicating procedures, exposures are determined using a through-the-lens light meter. In this case a flash meter could not be used. Once exposure has been determined by a test there is not much need for a light meter, providing that conditions remain the same.

The other disadvantage is related to expense. Inexpensive flash units, designed to be used on a camera, can be used as copying light sources. Some manufacturers make inexpensive electronic flash units that can be screwed into a standard light socket. Flash units are sold that have tungsten light sources (modeling lights) built-in to aid in lighting and focusing. These are usually more expensive than units without modeling lights. They are also more expensive than most tungsten lights. However, because photographic tungsten bulbs burn out after hours of usage, electronic flash may be less costly in the long run.

The table on this page shows what color film type and filter should be used for various light sources.

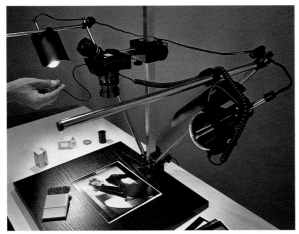

Copying with electronic flash. The flash unit on the right is synchronized with the camera. The unit on the left is equipped with a slave-triggering device that flashes the slave unit when the synchronized unit is fired.

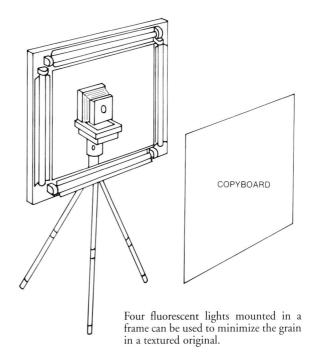

Four fluorescent lights mounted in a frame can be used to minimize the grain in a textured original.

Daylight: While the use of daylight cannot be recommended as a commercial procedure, it is quite feasible as a temporary expedient. The work can be done either outdoors or in a well-lit room. A skylight is an advantage if available. Since daylight is variable in both color quality and intensity, expose the negatives as near to midday as possible. When copying with color films, it is particularly important to avoid those times (two hours after sunrise, two hours before sunset) when the light has a yellowish cast. Use a combination of sun plus sky illumination. Open shade (skylight only) is bluish, as is the light on overcast days, although both can be corrected with a KODAK Color Compensating Filter. Remember that direct sunlight falling on the original may be affected by reflection from colored objects nearby.

Watch for variations in light caused by passing clouds. To assess correct exposure indoors and out, use a KODAK Gray Card at the copyboard in conjunction with an exposure meter.

Fluorescent: The color quality of most fluorescent lighting is unsuitable for use with color photographic materials. However, there are specially-rated fluorescent lamps which are designated as having a color temperature of 5400 K and a CRI (Color Rendering Index) rating of 98. They are designed for use with daylight-balanced color films. While such fluorescent tubes provide a light source which approximates daylight, the intensity of the light is low and may require long exposures especially if polarizing filters are used on the lights and/or the camera.

The diffuse nature of fluorescent lighting makes it particularly useful when the grain in copies from textured-surface originals must be eliminated. Four tubes, in suitable reflectors, are arranged to form a square, the sides of which are parallel to the edges of the copyboard. The length of the tubes and their distance from the board depends largely on the size of the original being copied. Since this lighting setup is not easy to adjust, it is most useful when originals do not vary much in size.

Fluorescent tubes have three advantages not possessed by most types of lighting; they generate very little heat, are relatively shadowless, and have a long working life. Use exposure times of 1/30 second and longer to avoid variations in exposure caused by the pulsating nature of fluorescent lights.

LAMP REPLACEMENT

When one lamp, for example, in a set of four copying lights burns out, a new replacement will almost certainly be brighter than the remaining three lamps. To avoid adjusting a new lamp to get uniform illumination on the copyboard, replace all four lamps. In copying with color films it is especially important to follow this procedure, because new lamps are not only brighter, but have a higher color temperature than those that have been burning for some time. Variations such as these result in uneven color balance over the picture area.

NOTE: The darkening of lamps that have been burning for some time occurs with ordinary tungsten lamps, but it is not a problem with tungsten-halogen lighting.

Voltage Regulators: Fluctuations in the voltage of electrical current are generally not serious in copying with black-and-white films, but because even modest fluctuation causes a change in the color quality and intensity of the copying lights, such changes can be troublesome with color materials. One solution to the problem is to install voltage regulators in the electrical supply to the lamps. Be sure, however, that any such units have the capacity to handle the electrical load placed upon them. In any case, get professional advice before taking action in regard to voltage fluctuation.

KODAK WRATTEN Gelatin Filters are available in all colors and in many degrees of filtering strength. A KODAK Gelatin Filter Frame Holder and a KODAK Gelatin Filter Frame are shown in the foreground.

Filters

Filters are used extensively in copying and duplicating work to improve the photographic result both in color and black and white. The action of a filter is to absorb light of certain colors. For example, a red filter transmits red light and absorbs or stops green and blue light. Any specific filter can be used only with films sensitive to the color of light transmitted by the filter. Generally, closely related hues are permitted to pass through while complementary colors are absorbed or stopped. When this occurs there is a change in both the color and intensity of the light going to expose the film. The proportion of the light absorbed or subtracted depends on the transmission characteristics of the filter, and affects the filter factor.

Filters reduce the light reaching the sensitized material and therefore an increase in exposure is usually required to compensate either by use of a larger aperture or a slower shutter speed. This change is expressed as a filter factor—a number that indicates how many times the exposure without a filter must be multiplied to obtain a satisfactory result with a filter. Filter factors are given on the Color Filter Circle on page 35 for most Kodak panchromatic films.

Filters, whether glass or gelatin (film or cemented), should be kept in dust-free, opaque containers in a cool, dry place. They should always be handled carefully by the edges and be kept free of scratches, dirt, or fingerprints to avoid serious loss in definition. The dyes used in some filters are only moderately stable and should not be exposed to daylight or fluorescent light for prolonged periods of time or subjected to extreme temperatures and humidities.

CLASSES OR TYPES OF FILTERS

There are a considerable number of filter types designed for specific purposes in black-and-white and color copying and duplicating. These are summarized briefly here. More detailed information can be found in *Using Filters*, Publication KW-13 and *KODAK Photographic Filters Handbook*, Publication B-3.

Contrast Filters: Filters offer one approach to contrast control with black-and-white copying, provided the original is multicolored. The less pure the colors involved, the less important is the possible filter effect and the more significant become factors such as film contrast, exposure, paper printing grade, and the degree of development. Selection of the most appropriate contrast filter demands considerable judgment and practical tests with several filters and films. Often viewing the original through several likely contrast filters will help, although the eye and film are not exactly alike in their color response. KODAK WRATTEN Gelatin Filters for reproducing common colors as lighter or darker include Nos. 12, 29, 47, 58, 25, 11, 13, and occasionally others.

As a general rule, filters lighten colors (in the final print) that are the same hue or a similar hue to the filter color, and darken colors that are complementary to the filter color. The filter circle on page 35 shows a variety of KODAK WRATTEN Filters, the colors that are lightened and darkened by them, and their filter factors for daylight and tungsten light.

Neutral Density Filters: Generally neutral density filters are used to increase the exposure time and can be used with any black-and-white or color film without materially altering contrast or color balance (in some uses, ND filters may add a slight amount of yellow to the neutrality). Neutral density filters are specified according to the transmission density of each filter. KODAK WRATTEN Neutral Density Filters No. 96 are manufactured in 1/3 *f*-stop increments from a density of .10 to 1.00 and in 1 1/3 *f*-stop increments from 1.00 to 4.00. The chart below shows the density of the filter, the percent transmission, and the increase in exposure that results from using each filter.

Neutral density filters can be used to make an exposure series without changing exposure time or aperture. They are also commonly used for flashing. If a 1% flash exposure to a white card is desired, a 2.00 KODAK WRATTEN Neutral Density Filter would be put in front of the lens. The flash exposure would be made for the same time and at the same *f*-number as the main exposure. More information on flashing is provided in the section "Controlling Contrast of Transparency Films" on page 78.

This copy was illuminated with tungsten light and copied on KODAK EKTACHROME 64 Film, which is daylight-balanced. The lack of balance results in an overall orangey color.

The lights and the film are the same, but a KODAK WRATTEN Gelatin Filter No. 80A has been used to balance the film to the lights.

KODACHROME 40 Film 5070 (Type A) is balanced for reflector-floods, which have a balance of 3400 K. This copy was made with studio lamps with a 3200 K balance, which has made the copy slightly warm.

The film and lights are the same for this copy, but it was made through a KODAK WRATTEN Gelatin Filter No. 82A, which, in the copy, gives a close approximation of the colors in the original print.

Exact color balance is often achieved using color compensating (CC) filters. This copy was illuminated with studio lights (3200 K) and copied on KODAK EKTACHROME 50 Professional Film (Tungsten). This should have given a balanced copy, but the copy is actually slightly more magenta than the original.

This copy was made through a 10 green color compensating filter (CC10G) which has corrected the color balance. The exact original film balance, film aging, the camera lens, the lamp reflectors, the walls in the copy area can all contribute to a lack of exact color balance in copies. Continual monitoring of results is the one way to ensure consistent color balance.

FILTERS IN ENLARGERS

Many color enlargers are equipped with cyan, magenta, and yellow dichroic filters. A dichroic filter is made by evaporating multilayered coatings on a substrate such as glass. They work using the interference principle of light. The advantage of dichroic filters is that they are sharp-cutting, so that they are more optically effective than gelatin filters and withstand heat better than gelatin filters, and their use makes the use of filter dials for color control more practical.

Enlarger light sources equipped with such filters can be used as light sources for many color duplicating operations. The color of the light source is adjusted using the dichroic filter controls and no other filters are required.

Another type of enlarger light source uses three light sources, one red, one green, and one blue. The light is mixed to create white light. The balance of the white light is adjusted by controlling the intensity of each of these lights. This type of enlarger head can also be used as a light source for color duplication. In some automatic printers, balance is achieved by automatic adjustment of the time the filters are inserted into the light beam.

BLACK-AND-WHITE COPYING TECHNIQUES

Copying of photographs to make high-quality copies is often considered a straightforward, simple task. In reality there are few jobs in photography that place such high demands on the skill and patience of the photographer. To make good copies from the many different types of originals requires a knowledge of the techniques and materials that yield the best result in a given situation.

As indicated in the glossary, copying refers to the making of a photograph of a reflection-type image. Commonly a photographic negative is made either in black and white or color. However, making transparencies of reflection originals is also considered to be copying. Making transparent images of transparent negatives or positive transparencies is considered duplicating, and this subject is covered in the section entitled "Duplicating."

Reflection copy originals include a wide variety of subject matter broadly divided into line originals and continuous-tone originals. They may be either black and white or color. They vary in size from very small to very large. Line originals include printed matter, drawings, typewritten originals, handwritten manuscripts, faded manuscripts, documents on yellowed paper (such as old newsprint), blueprints, and colored line originals.

Continuous-tone originals include photographs, crayon and chalk drawings, acrylic, watercolor and oil paintings, halftones*, and stained prints. Another group of continuous-tone originals includes old and/or damaged photographic prints, daguerreotypes, faded prints, ambrotypes, tintypes, and calotypes. There are also some reflection originals that are described as combined line and continuous-tone originals.

Preparation of Originals for Copying

Originals should be handled with the greatest of care and not be subjected to potential damage or loss. They may be historically valuable, irreplaceable, or of sentimental value. The best copy negative possible should be made before attempting any pre-copy treatment. Of course, originals in good condition require no preparation. If any pre-treatment is necessary, it is important to get written approval from the owner in case any damage to the original results from the treatment.

Reflections from Buckled or Creased Prints:
Originals with a buckled or creased surface are a special problem in copying because they tend to reflect the copying lights in many directions. Ordinary photographic prints that are new or fairly new can be soaked in water and dried between photographic blotters to remove buckles and creases. Do not re-ferrotype a glossy print, because it may stick to the ferrotyping surface and become a total loss. Remember to spot the print if necessary, because the original spotting may have washed off.

If it is not advisable to wet the original completely, creases can often be removed or reduced by dampening the back of the print and then flattening it in a dry mounting press heated to a lower temperature than that used for mounting: approximately 100°F (28°C). The use of polarized light when copying is often helpful in minimizing reflections from buckled prints. Double polarization is often necessary in this instance. (See the section on page 53.)

Valuable originals must be handled carefully. Here an antique carte-de-visite is being blown off with an air duster prior to copying.

Old photographs may be daguerreotypes, tintypes, albumin prints, ambrotypes, salted paper prints, or old gelatin silver prints made on gas-light paper. All should be handled with great care to avoid damage.

*While halftone originals are technically line originals, they are usually treated as continuous-tone originals in copying.

Cleaning Prints Before Copying: Careful examination of the original under a bright light may reveal surface defects, discoloration, stains, grease spots, dirt, dust, etc. As indicated previously, an examination may indicate the need to clean, restore, or retouch the original and permission should be obtained from the owner. In any case the need to make a copy is the first requirement. This point cannot be overemphasized.

Dust and lint can be removed by gently brushing the original with a camel's-hair brush and an air syringe. An artist's kneaded rubber eraser or a gum eraser used lightly will remove dirt and light marks. Erasers or any other abrasive, however, should not be used on an old original or on a valuable photograph. Chemical deposits from the eraser or the abrasion itself may cause harm to the photographic image in time.

Beyond this preliminary examination and cleaning there may be need for some corrective measures such as retouching. Handwork can often be done on the original but it is generally safer to do the work on the copy negative or a print made from the copy negative. Then make a new copy negative from which the final copy print is made.

The Copying Procedure

The original to be copied is placed on the copyboard and centered with the optical axis of the copy camera. Lines drawn on the copyboard help to center the original and to align the edges vertically and horizontally when copying on a horizontal copy stand. The edges are aligned with the camera when copying vertically. The original is held in place on a vacuum board, or with magnetic strips, finger-type spring clamps, or a plate of glass placed over the original.

Next, the image of the copy must be sized and focused by viewing the image on the viewing screen or through the SLR viewfinder. When making copies at low magnification (greater than about 1:3 ratio of image size to original size), sizing is done by adjusting the camera-to-copyboard distance, while focusing is done using the camera adjustments. On a small-format camera the focusing is done with the helical focusing ring. Focusing on a view camera is done by adjusting the front or rear standard forward or backward.

Sizing and focusing at high magnification (about 1:2 or greater) is performed the opposite way. Sizing is controlled by changing the lens-to-film distance, and focusing is accomplished by changing the camera-to-copyboard distance. This adjustment can be made by either moving the camera or the copyboard.

To estimate the lens-to-film distance for a given magnification, use the following formula:

Lens-to-Film Distance
= (Magnification + 1) x Focal Length

Example: Magnification desired - 1:1 or 1X
Focal length of lens - 6 inches
Lens-to-Film Distance = (1 + 1) x 6 inches
= 12 inches

Magnification is sometimes expressed as the image size divided by the subject size (i.e. 2:1, 3:1, 1:2) and sometimes by the value of the ratio (2:1 = 2X, 3:1 = 3X, 1:2 = 0.5X).

Because it is not always possible to determine the optical center of a lens (principal point), the precise lens-to-film distance can only be estimated. To check the magnification ratio accurately, the image size on the ground glass must be measured and compared to the subject (object) size.

Commonly, the copy photographer must make a negative where the image must measure a certain length (the magnification is not specified). In this case, just measure the image on the ground glass when sizing and focusing.

The next step is to provide even illumination on the copyboard.

Lighting

On page 17 is a section that describes various types of light sources commonly used for copying. In this section we discussed various arrangements of the lights to achieve even illumination, the need for even illumination on the copyboard, and methods of measuring to determine whether the light distribution is uniform.

Lamp Arrangement: Small originals—up to 8 x 10 inches—can be illuminated with two lamps placed about 30 inches from the center of the copyboard and at an angle of about 45 degrees to the lens axis (see illustration). This angle can be varied somewhat if it is necessary to avoid reflections in a cover glass, but it is important that both lamps be at the same angle.

Four lamps, one at each corner of the copyboard, provide a better spread of light than the two-lamp setup just described and, at the same time, can be adjusted to give a little extra light intensity at the corners of the board where it is needed to offset the effects of lens falloff.

Specially designed copy cameras are equipped with lights that illuminate adequately a range of original sizes. However, these lights are adjustable, and the foregoing remarks about copyboard illumination apply equally to the more elaborate equipment.

If the illumination on an original being copied is uneven, both the copy negative and print will show the results of this unevenness. This is true both when making continuous-tone copies and high-contrast copies of line originals.

Control of Illumination: The easiest method to get even copyboard illumination is to begin with lights of the same wattage and measure the intensity of one light (or bank of lights) at a time. The light intensity is then equalized usually by moving the lights closer or farther away from the copyboard at the same angle.

First aim the beam of one light (or bank of lights) at the far side of the copyboard. Then place a KODAK Gray Card on the center of the copyboard and take a light meter reading with a reflected-type light meter. The reading can be made directly from the camera if it has a through-the-lens meter. Turn off the light and repeat the procedure with the other light. Adjust the distance of the lights until each light separately gives the same light meter reading at the center of the copyboard.

The individual light readings can also be measured with an incident light meter that has a hemispherical light diffuser. The light meter is placed in the center of the copyboard parallel to the copyboard for the readings.

The third method is to use an incident meter equipped with a flat diffusing disc. The light meter can measure the individual light intensity by pointing it toward each light. Both lights can be on during the light measurements.

If all the originals to be copied are small, the lamps with either a 2-lamp or 4-lamp setup can be aimed at the center of the copyboard. This will give a high level of illumination and keep the exposures relatively short.

However, even when an original is illuminated uniformly over its entire surface, it does not follow that a negative made from it will be uniformly exposed (as discussed on page 16). This effect is most noticeable with large originals. If a smaller aperture or a lens of longer focal length cannot yield uniform exposure, the alternative is to adjust copyboard illumination by increasing the light intensity at the edges. The amount of this increase can be measured by taking light meter readings in the conventional manner at the copyboard, or by taking light measurements at the focal plane. A light meter for measuring light at the focal plane of large-format cameras is illustrated below. This type of meter consists of a light-sensitive cell mounted at the end of a rigid, moveable probe, which is connected to the exposure meter. The meter can also be used to calculate exposure by measuring copyboard illumination with the gray side of the KODAK Gray Card placed on the copyboard. Be sure to stop the lens down to the working aperture before taking measurements.

When the most even illumination has been found, mark or record the position of the lights so that the conditions can be repeated when necessary. Because the optical image in the camera is measured, no change in exposure for magnification should be made when calculating exposure.

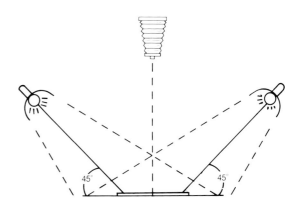

A more even distribution of light across the copyboard may be achieved by aiming the center of the light beam nearer to the edges of the copy area rather than at the center.

A special probe is made to be attached to a handheld exposure meter so that illumination at the ground glass of view cameras can be measured. With ground-glass metering, the consistency of the lighting across the focal plane can be measured. By adjusting the lights on the copyboard, the light as imaged by the lens can be made even. The ground-glass meter can also be used to measure the image of a gray card, or of highlights or shadows as an aid to getting correct exposure.

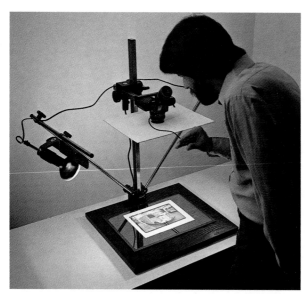

When copying vertically, a piece of clean glass can be used to hold the copy flat. A camera reflection shield, black on the lower side, can be used to avoid a reflection of the camera in the glass. Using polarizing filters is also useful. Notice the image being copied has a white border. In this case, it is being included in the copy photograph. Otherwise, it would be covered with black paper or board to help eliminate flare.

The reflection shield is shown in detail. A hole in the center of the card is cut to just fit the camera lens. A filter step-up ring is recommended to keep the card from slipping off of the lens, although black photographic masking tape can be used to attach the card to the lens, if necessary.

Slight fall off of illumination at the focal plane is not usually serious when copying continuous-tone originals. In fact, the effect is often compensated by a similar effect in the optical system of an enlarger. However, when high-contrast film is being used to copy line originals, the effect of differences in light intensity is increased by the short exposure latitude of the film. In this situation, illumination should be adjusted to give the best possible consistency across the focal plane.

Control of Light Around the Copy Setup: Good control of the illumination on and around the copyboard is necessary for consistent high-quality copies. Avoid copying near a window or a white wall. Both may cause a reflection in the surface of the original being copied that would show up in the copy print. Also, both might shine into the camera lens, raising the flare level. It is also a good idea to turn off the room lights, or at least to shield the copy area from them, for the same reasons.

Copying an Original Under Glass: When glass is used to hold an original flat, care must be taken to prevent unwanted reflections from the glass. The most common source of reflections is the camera or tripod. Sometimes these reflections go unnoticed when shooting but appear in the negative or transparency. The reflections may not be noticed, because when focusing at a wide aperture, they are out of focus. When the exposure is made at a much smaller aperture, they are brought into focus, much to the photographer's dismay.

To prevent the glass reflection problem, a black piece of cardboard with a hole cut out in the middle is placed over the lens. The cardboard should be big enough to cover all reflective parts of the camera. In a vertical copying situation the cardboard can be held on with a lens shade. When a large piece of glass is used with a large copy, reflections can be caused by the tripod. A skirt made from a black focusing cloth will eliminate these reflections.

Dust is another problem encountered when using glass to hold down an original. The sheet of glass provides an extra two surfaces which can attract dust. For all these reasons, it is best to avoid using glass if possible.

Flare: Flare is non-image-forming light that exposes film. It is caused by reflection of light from lens surfaces, the interior edges of lens mounts, diaphragm blades, and the interiors of cameras. Bright areas near the copy area, such as a white copyboard, windows, and room lights are likely to raise the flare level.

Flare light lowers the contrast of the optical image, because light from the brighter portions of the subject (copy original and copyboard) is spread over the entire image and adds more exposure (as a percentage of the total) to the darker sections of the image. It also tends to reduce the apparent sharpness of the recorded detail.

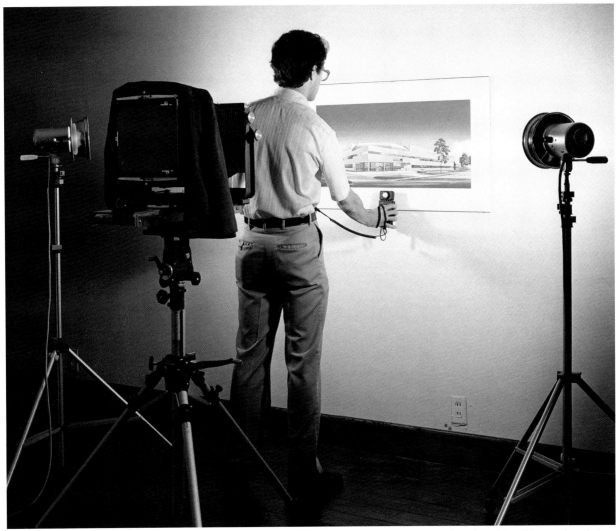

Lighting consistency from top to bottom and from left to right is especially critical with large originals such as this architectural rendering.

Some newer exposure meters incorporate an electronic calculator instead of the dial calculator. With this type of meter you set the meter for the film speed, choose the shutter speed desired, and take the light reading. The meter then reads out the *f*-stop required.

When a camera that has a through-the-lens meter is used, a gray card is placed on the copyboard as it would be for a handheld reflected-type meter. The reading is taken directly from the card. If the original is large and the gray card occupies a small portion of the frame, the camera should be moved in close to the card to take the reading so that the card fills the frame. Do not change the focus when taking the reading or an inaccurate reading may be obtained due to an increase in lens-to-film distance (this is discussed later in more detail). Use of a spot meter makes it easier to measure the gray card from a distance.

A good method to use when copying printed text material is to measure a white card and to give 5X the exposure indicated by the card, or an increase of 2 1/3 stops. If the printed material is measured, meter readings will vary as the size, weight, or amount of text on each page varies, while the exposure required remains constant. The white card method compensates for this.

When electronic flash is used as a light source, a flash meter can be used to determine exposure. Flash meters are used in a manner similar to that used with conventional light meters except that the only camera adjustment indicated is the *f*-stop.

Once you have measured the light with a light meter and have an *f*-stop/shutter speed combination, you have determined the basic exposure. This basic exposure is modified by making adjustments for magnification, filter factors, and reciprocity law failure before a negative can be exposed.

Determining Basic Exposure with Tests: To determine a basic exposure without a light meter, run a series of tests with the film or films to be used. Use the table below to estimate a starting exposure time. Don't forget to include in your exposure calculations a factor for magnification (bellows extension) if necessary.

From the test series, choose a negative that makes a good reproduction of the original on a normal grade of photographic paper. Record the exposure time, the position of the lights, the lens aperture, the film speed, and the magnification for future reference.

Magnification: The most significant exposure compensation in copying occurs when the lens-to-film distance (often referred to as bellows extension or lens extension) becomes greater than the focal length of the lens. Lens-to-film distance increases rapidly as the reproduction size approaches 100 percent. In this situation, the copy negative image is the same size as the original, the lens-to-film distance is twice the focal length of the lens, and the exposure increase is four times that required with the lens focused at infinity. This is because the lens is twice as far away from the film as it is at infinity focus, and the effective *f*-numbers are twice the marked values. For example, *f*/16 becomes *f*/8 at 1:1 magnification, requiring 4X the exposure time.

When a handheld meter is used to calculate the exposure, or when a standard exposure has been found by running tests, an exposure factor for lens extension must be considered to achieve proper exposure when a bellows camera is being used.

However, when close-focusing is achieved by using a close-up lens (diopter) in front of the camera lens, no additional exposure is required. When a camera that has through-the-lens metering is used, no additional exposure is required for magnification when the exposure is determined by the camera meter.

Next to using TTL metering to set exposure, the simplest way to find the exposure factor is by the magnification method. Magnification is the ratio of the image size divided by the subject size. A common method of finding magnification is to use a 1-inch subject (such as that provided in the margin) placed

on the copyboard. The focusing screen (ground glass) image of the copy is first sized and focused. The 1-inch target is placed on the copyboard. The size of the ground glass image of this target is measured. The magnification is found by dividing the image size by the object size. In this case, the image size is divided by 1, so the image size itself is the magnification.

The exposure factor is found mathematically using the equation:

$$\text{Exposure Factor} = (\text{Magnification} + 1)^2$$

You can find the exposure factors for the common copying range of magnifications using the graph on the next page. The horizontal scale is calibrated both in magnification values and image size values when a 1-inch target is used. There is also a dial in *KODAK Professional Photoguide*, Publication R-28, that helps find exposure factors.

Another method commonly used with bellows-type cameras to find the exposure factor is to measure the lens-to-film distance and use the formula below. F is the focal length of the lens and B is the lens-to-film distance (bellows).

$$\frac{(\text{Lens-to-Film Distance})^2}{(\text{Focal Length})^2} = \frac{B^2}{F^2} = \text{Exposure Factor}$$

The lens-to-film distance should be measured from the approximate center of the lens to the ground glass. For example, when an 8-inch lens (210 mm) is used with a 4 x 5 camera to copy a print, a 12-inch bellows distance results. To figure out the additional exposure time necessary, the preceding formula is used.

$$\frac{(12)^2}{(8)^2} = \text{Exposure Factor} \quad \frac{144}{64} = 2.25$$

If the calculated exposure is 1 second, the corrected exposure time would be 2 1/4 seconds. If the film being used has a reciprocity correction necessary at 2 1/4 seconds, this should be considered (discussed in a later section).

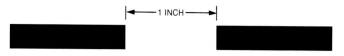

|← 1 INCH →|

Starting Point Exposures for Test Negatives

Individual Lamp Wattage*	400	320	250	200	125	100	80	50	32	25	12	8
					Film Speeds							
1000 W	f/64	f/56	f/50	f/45	f/35	f/32	f/29	f/22	f/18	f/16	f/11	f/9
500 W	f/45	f/40	f/35	f/32	f/24.5	f/22	f/20	f/16	f/12.5	f/11	f/8	f/6.8
250 W	f/32	f/28	f/24.5	f/22	f/17.5	f/16	f/15	f/11	f/9	f/8	f/5.6	f/4.5

*The chart is based upon the use of two lights, three feet from the copyboard, at an angle of 45° and a shutter speed of ½ sec.

MAGNIFICATION EXPOSURE ADJUSTMENT CHART

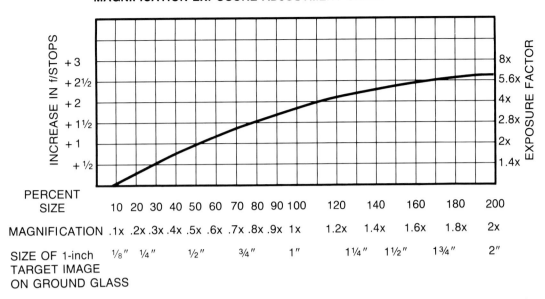

| PERCENT SIZE | 10 20 30 40 50 60 70 80 90 100 | 120 | 140 | 160 | 180 | 200 |

MAGNIFICATION .1x .2x .3x .4x .5x .6x .7x .8x .9x 1x   1.2x   1.4x   1.6x   1.8x   2x

SIZE OF 1-inch TARGET IMAGE ON GROUND GLASS: ⅛″ ¼″ ½″ ¾″ 1″ 1¼″ 1½″ 1¾″ 2″

This graph can be used to adjust indicated exposures as found by metering or a test for changes in magnification. Adjustment for reciprocity may be needed in addition when long exposure times are required.

Filter Factors: Filters are frequently used in black-and-white copying to help eliminate stains in the copy or to increase contrast. Using a filter also requires increasing the exposure. The filter circle below shows the filter factors required for various colored KODAK WRATTEN Filters when used with normal KODAK Panchromatic Films such as KODAK PLUS-X Pan Film, KODAK EKTAPAN Film 4162 (ESTAR Thick Base), and KODAK T-MAX Professional Films.

Multiply the filter factor by the correct exposure time without a filter to find the exposure time with the filter. For example, if the filter factor is 8X and the exposure time without a filter is 1 second, the exposure time with the filter is 8 seconds. As with lens extension exposure factors, an additional correction may be required due to the reciprocity characteristics of film.

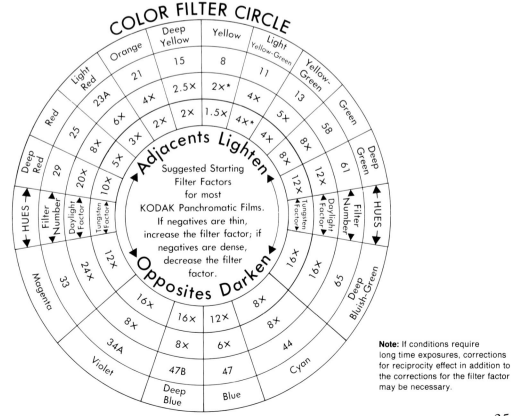

*For a gray-tone rendering of colors approximating their visual brightnesses.

Note: If conditions require long time exposures, corrections for reciprocity effect in addition to the corrections for the filter factor may be necessary.

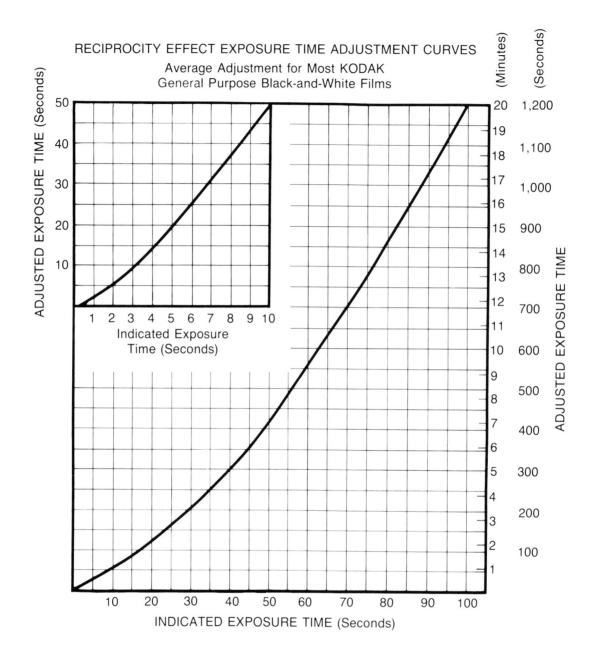

RECIPROCITY EFFECT EXPOSURE TIME ADJUSTMENT CURVES
Average Adjustment for Most KODAK
General Purpose Black-and-White Films

Reciprocity Law: The reciprocity law failure effect, sometimes incorrectly called "reciprocity," is frequently encountered in copying. The law of reciprocity is the principle that allows a photographer to choose among many different *f*-stop and shutter speed combinations at one light level and get essentially the same exposure at all combinations. For example, when taking pictures outdoors with a fast film, an exposure of *f*/16 at 1/250 second might be indicated by your light meter. An equivalent exposure would be obtained using *f*/11 at 1/500 second or *f*/22 at 1/125 second. The reciprocity law is stated as Exposure = Illuminance x Time.

The reciprocity law applies to most films except for extremely short and extremely long exposure times. During extremely long or short exposure times the equation E = IT can become invalid and reciprocity law "failure" occurs. This means that two equivalent *f*-stop/shutter speed combinations will not produce equal results. Usually, an increase in exposure and less development is required for long exposure times. All films do not respond exactly the same.

Because bellows factors, filter factors, slow film speeds, and relatively small apertures are used in copying, long exposure times are frequently required. Exposures longer than one second usually require a reciprocity law failure adjustment with most films. Adjustment means an increase in exposure, either by lengthening the exposure time or opening up the diaphragm. The graph shows the reciprocity law failure exposure time adjustments for many Kodak black-and-white films.

EXPOSING KODAK PROFESSIONAL COPY FILM 4125

With ordinary black-and-white films, the contrast of negatives is controlled by development. However, with KODAK Professional Copy Film 4125, contrast in the copy negative is controlled by both development and exposure.

Development controls the contrast of the midtone and dark-tone (shadow) regions of the negative, (and to a slight extent, the highlight region) while exposure primarily controls the contrast of the light-tone region and the density range of the negative.

To determine the correct developing time for your conditions, a test can be performed to find the best exposure-development combination. Using a tray process and KODAK HC-110 Developer (Dilution E), the development time range is from 3 to 5 minutes. To find which of these times gives the midtone and dark-tone (shadow) contrast suitable for your equipment, run a test of five negatives developed at 3, 3 1/2, 4, 4 1/2, and 5 minutes. If you are using a large tank, the times would be 4, 4 1/2, 5, 5 1/2, and 6 minutes. Expose the test negative to an original that has a contrast range that is typical of the type of originals to be copied. It is helpful if the original has a few large representative light, medium, and dark tones. Print the negatives using your enlarger and paper that you plan to use, and select the negative that gives the midtone and dark-tone contrast you prefer.

Repeat the test, but vary the exposure and keep the development constant. Varying the exposure changes the ratio of tones recorded on the two portions of the characteristic curve. Negatives with less exposure will have more of the midtones recorded with normal contrast and fewer of the light tones and highlights recorded with increased contrast. Negatives with more exposure will have more of the midtones recorded with higher contrast. Make prints, and select the print which appears to have the best overall tonal quality. This determines the basic exposure to use. Using a KODAK Gray Card and an exposure meter, calculate backwards to get an exposure index that gives this type of copy negative.

For example, if the meter measurement of the card gives a value of 8, set the meter calculator at this value. Your exposure was 2 seconds at f/16. Adjust the calculator as you would set film speed until the exposure of 2 seconds at f/16 shows on the dial. By making several adjustments, you find the exposure index is 12. Use this value for future tests.

If a photograph to be copied has turned an even brownish tone, it helps to copy it through a blue filter, such as a KODAK WRATTEN Filter No. 47 or No. 47B. Although there are no recommended filter factors for this film, a factor of about 10X (3 1/4 stops) for the No. 47 filter and 20X (4 1/4 stops) for

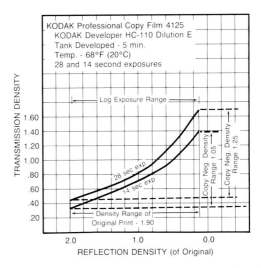

This graph shows how copy negative density range is adjusted by changing the copy exposure when using KODAK Professional Copy Film. The curves are specific examples of 14-second and 28-second exposure times. Lighting and f-number are constant.

the 47B with tungsten light should be a good starting point. With lights that have a daylight balance, a factor of about 6X (2 1/2 stops) for the 47 and 12X (3 1/2 stops) for the 47B should be close.

Once a basic exposure is found that produces good tone reproduction when the copy negative is printed on a normal-grade paper, the same exposure can be given when copying nearly all continuous-tone originals. Adjustments are made, of course, for changes in magnification.

By giving the same exposure, the highlight tones are consistently placed in the upsweep part of the curve, while the midtones and dark tones are recorded on the lower, straight-line portion of the curve.

When using KODAK Professional Copy Film 4125, it is important to place the white tones on the same place on the characteristic curve of the copy film. For negatives to be printed on diffusion enlargers, a copy negative should have a maximum density (image of the whites) of about 1.20, which gives a copy negative density range of about 0.95 when a full-scale print (reflection density range of about 1.65) is being copied.

When short-scale prints are being copied, there are two approaches. If the short-scale print (low reflection-density range) is short-scale because the subject was low in contrast, give the same exposure that you would to a full-scale print. The copy print will then come close to having the same tonal range of the original.

However, if the short-scale print is low in contrast as a result of fading, you want the copy print to have normal contrast. If the print looks like the low-contrast print illustrated on page 60, increase the exposure on professional copy film to increase the D-max and the copy negative density range to improve the contrast in the copy print. 1/2- to 1-stop increase in exposure should give the desired results.

These two illustrations are intended to show the difference between continuous tone and a halftone image; actually the reproduction above is a very-fine-screen halftone—a continuous-tone image cannot be printed by offset lithography.

This halftone has a screen coarse enough to be readily seen. The black dots in light tones are small. Dark tones are small white dots in an all-black surround. The halftone dot size is controlled by the original print tones when the halftone is made.

Be sure to adjust the exposure for magnification and reciprocity changes, if necessary.

You may want to try both methods to see which method meets your particular needs.

KODAK Professional Copy Film 4125 is an orthochromatic film and cannot be used with orange or red filters. Further, this film is not generally recommended for copying colored originals. Reds will copy much darker than they appear. KODAK EKTAPAN Film 4162 in sheets, KODAK Technical Pan Film 2415, KODAK PLUS-X Pan and PLUS-X Pan Professional Films in rolls are recommended for red-filter copying and copying colored originals in black and white.

KODAK Commercial Film 4127 is a blue-sensitive film. Without a filter it responds as if a blue filter were being used, making it a good film to use to copy overall brownish or yellowish faded prints. It also responds well to increasing developing times to increase contrast.

Exposing Line Negatives: An original that consists of tones that are only pure black and pure white is a line original. A line original must be exposed on high-contrast film and processed in a high-contrast developer if a reproduction that looks like the original is desired.

When many line negatives are to be made it is a good idea to establish a basic exposure as was done with continuous-tone copies. There are some aspects about line copying that are different from continuous-tone copying.

When choosing an original to establish the basic exposure, select an original that has good, rich blacks and clean, bright whites. A piece of type printed on smooth shiny paper is best. Be sure the type has clean, sharp edges.

Your exposure can be determined with a light meter or by trial and error tests. To find a starting point for tests, consult the chart on page 34 and select an exposure based on the film speed of the high-contrast film being used and the wattage of the light sources.

When a light meter is used to determine exposure, the readings can be made with a gray card and reflected-light meter, or with an incident meter and the indicated exposure is given. If a white card (instead of a gray card) is used with a reflected-light meter, give 5X the indicated exposure (an increase of 2 1/3 stops) as a starting exposure. This is to place the white in the highlight region of the film. The same exposure corrections for magnification, filter factors, and reciprocity failure apply to line and continuous-tone copying. Do not forget to include these factors when making your first test.

Illustration Idea

With a little study and practice, the technical end of making photographs becomes natural and even easy. It is solving problems and translating ideas into successful photographs that makes photo illustrations a challenging, enjoyable, and lucrative way of making a living.

The photographs presented here are examples of ideas brought to successful conclusions through

This series of three illustrations is intended to show the effect of exposure on a line copy image. The illustration above received a correct exposure.

Illustration Idea

With a little study and practice, the technical end of making photographs becomes natural and even easy. It is solving problems and translating ideas into successful photographs that makes photo illustrations a challenging, enjoyable, and lucrative way of making a living.

The photographs presented here are examples of ideas brought to successful conclusions through

Illustration Idea

With a little study and practice, the technical end of making photographs becomes natural and even easy. It is solving problems and translating ideas into successful photographs that makes photo illustrations a challenging, enjoyable, and lucrative way of making a living.

The photographs presented here are examples of ideas brought to successful conclusions through

This copy print was made from an overexposed line negative. Notice how the lines have thinned and how the letters in the text have become weak.

In a print made from an underexposed line negative, the lines have broadened, and in some cases, run together. In the lower portion, the background density in the negative is too light, so that some tone shows in the print.

A good line negative will have clear shadow areas (black on the original) and opaque highlights (white on the original) with few pinholes. (Pinholes are tiny, clear areas in the dense portion of the negative. Some almost always occur on high-contrast films.) It will maintain the same edge sharpness as the original and the same line thickness relationships. In other words, type won't have fuzzy edges, and the characters will be the same thickness in proportion to the original.

In the illustrations on page 39, prints were made from an underexposed line negative, a good negative, and an overexposed negative. The underexposed line negative has an excessive amount of pinholes and does not have a high-enough density in the highlight area. The normal negative makes a print with sharp black lines on a clean white background. The overexposed negative makes a print that loses sharpness and detail. The overexposure caused thin lines to fill in completely on the negative and sharp thick lines to become fuzzy. This is because overexposure causes areas to gain density that should have remained clear.

When a basic exposure has been established that produces a good line negative, this exposure can be used to calculate exposures for most other line negatives. The factors for magnification changes, filters, and reciprocity must be included in the calculations, and the lighting and processing conditions should remain constant.

Some variations in negative quality can occur from negative to negative if the whiteness of the original paper stock is not consistent. To compensate for the differences in the whiteness of originals, a reflected-light meter can be used to read the exposure from the original. The reading must be taken from a portion of the original that has no type on it. A blank piece of paper of the same type as the original, or the back of the original, can also be used. A spot meter may be helpful in this situation. An exposure 5 times the calculated exposure is used as a starting exposure. For example, if the exposure is calculated to be 1 second at ƒ16 (based on the reading of a white portion of the original) the actual exposure would be about 5 seconds at ƒ16. As mentioned earlier, the indicated exposure is multiplied by 5 to find the correct exposure. A check should be made to see whether a correction should be made for reciprocity law failure.

Processing Black-and-White Copy Negatives

The procedures of processing rolls and sheets of copy negatives are just the same as those for processing regular negatives. These procedures are discussed in detail in *KODAK Professional Black-and-White Films*, Publication F-5, and are not repeated here. However, some aspects of processing that pertain especially to copy negatives are important to review.

CHOOSING THE DEVELOPER

There are several possible developers that can be used for most of the films discussed in this publication. Information sheets supplied with the film usually offer a choice of several developers with recommended developing times for each.

When developing in a tank, it is appropriate to choose one of the recommended developers and dilutions that gives a developing time of five minutes or longer to aid in achieving uniformity of development.

When developing sheet films in a tray, on the other hand, choosing a developer and dilution that gives a moderately short developing time can speed up the process with less likelihood of poor development uniformity.

Uniformity of Development: If an exposure of an evenly lit gray card is made and the film is processed, you would expect to get an even density across the negative. However, especially with copy films, you may find that the density varies across the negative, usually due to agitation effects during development. This shows up more on copy negatives because they are usually developed to a higher contrast than normal negatives. There are two types of nonuniformity encountered.

Random Mottle: If there is a random variation in density that gives a mottled appearance, the negative has usually received inadequate agitation. Increasing the degree, duration, or frequency of the agitation will usually correct this type of uneven density, except with very dilute developers.

High-Edge Density: When two opposite edges of the negative have higher density than the center of the negative, the negative has received too much agitation. While this effect usually results from agitation that is too vigorous, it can also occur from agitation that is too frequent or too long.

DEVELOPING PROCEDURES

Some people have found that developing sheet films with hangers in a small tank (one that just fits the hangers) leads to uneven development. Switching from a 4x5-inch tank to an 8x10-inch tank for 4x5-inch films, for example, has been found to make the development more uniform. This is because the larger developer surface area gives less swirl to the developer as the films are agitated.

The recommended procedure for roll films on spiral reels in small tanks is to agitate for 5 seconds every 30 seconds. To aid uniformity, the developer is put in the tank first, and in the dark, the loaded reel is lowered into the developer. The tank lid is put on the tank, and the tank is tapped several times on a firm surface to loosen air bells. Agitate for up to 4 cycles using the method appropriate for your tank. Do not agitate for the rest of the first 30 seconds. At the 30-second point, do a 5-second agitation cycle. From here on, at 30-second intervals, repeat 5-second agitation cycles for the duration of development. A special procedure is recommended for developing KODAK Technical Pan Film rolls. See page 60.

Several reels of roll film can be developed at a time in a deep tank normally used for sheet films. The reels are strung on a hanger rod and lowered into the developer. Agitation is accomplished by raising and rotating the rod. It is not necessary to lift the reels out of the developer. Agitate for 5 seconds at 1-minute intervals. After agitation, lower the reels slowly to the bottom of the tank.

Equipment commonly used for small-batch film processing. The processing trays at upper left are used for sheet film processing, as are the tank and sheet film hangers at upper right. In the front area are reels and tanks used for roll-film processing.

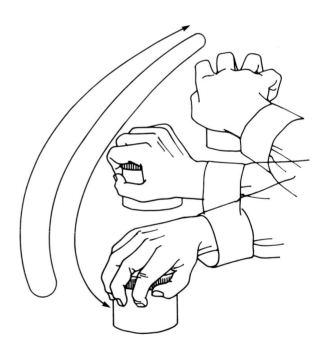

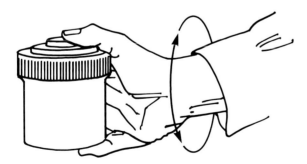

Agitation Method for an Inversion Tank

This type of agitation is called axial inversion because the tank is rotated 180° about an imaginary axis through the center of the tank. Although this method was developed specifically for developing KODAK Technical Pan Film, it is now believed that it gives more even results with all roll films.

Agitation Method for a Noninversion Tank

If the roll-film tank cannot be inverted without losing the solution, a horizontal agitation method can be used. The tank is moved back and forth as shown on a flat surface such as a sink bottom with enough force to cause the solution to move back and forth in the tank. Four back and forth movements make one cycle. Cycles are repeated at 30-second intervals. The tank is rotated 90° between each cycle so that the direction of the solution movement is changed.

Insertion Methods For Tray Developing Sheet Films

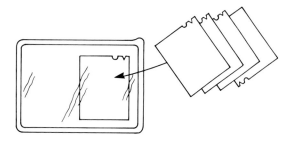

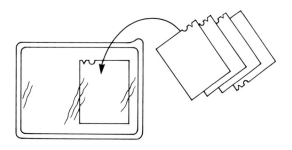

Insertion Methods for Tray-Developing Sheet Films
When using interleaving continuous agitation in the tray-development of sheet films, it is important to go through the stack completely. The first film in the developer is rotated 180° from the rest of the stack so that the notches are at the opposite end. This identifies it as the first film in so that it becomes the first film out, ensuring an equal time of development for each film.

Agitation Technique for Sheet-Film Hangers in a Large Tank

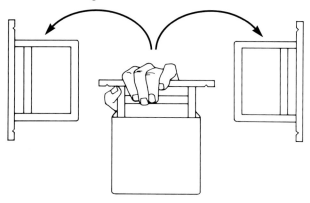

Agitation Technique for Sheet Film Hangers in a Large Tank
Lift the hanger, tilt it 90° to the left, replace it in tank. Lift it again, tilt it 90° to the right, and replace it in tank. Repeat once each minute.

The agitation movements of sheet film hangers in tank development. One cycle is described. In large tank development, the agitation cycle is repeated at 1-minute intervals. Both hands may be used to hold the hangers.

When tray-developing sheet films in quantity, the interleaving procedure is recommended. A water bath is prepared at the same temperature as the developer. The films are placed in the water, one at a time, emulsion-side down. The stack is turned over so that emulsions are facing upward, then the films are interleaved by placing the bottom film on the top of the stack. When the stack is back to its original order, the films are placed in the developer one at a time by the interleaving procedure—that is, the bottom film is removed and placed in the developer emulsion-side up. Each successive bottom film is placed on top of the stack. When all are in the developer, the interleaving continues, bottom to top, for the duration of the developing time. They are then interleaved into the stop bath in the same order, bottom to top.

Another method is to place the films in the developer, emulsion-side up. Each film is placed under the previous ones. When the stack of films is complete, start interleaving by taking the bottom film out and placing it on top of the stack. This is repeated continuously for the development period.

Some people keep count of the number of rotations so that each sheet of film receives equal development, and the "first-in, first-out" procedure can be used. Others snip off a corner of the first film so that it can be detected in the dark by feel. A third method is to turn the first film 180° so that the notches are in a different corner than the other sheets (see illustration).

When developing a single sheet of film, agitation is accomplished by rocking the tray. Lift each side of the tray alternately to produce a random motion to the waves of developer that provide the agitation.

OTHER PROCESSING PATTERNS

When films are processed in a vertical position and given inadequate agitation, a condition called "bromide drag" sometimes occurs. If a dense area is above a low-density area, bromide released by development of the dense area drops down over the less-dense area, inhibiting development. This shows as less-dense "streaks" in the lower area. The prevention is proper agitation.

Another directional effect sometimes occurs from physical variations in the film or in film hangers. If perforated film is overagitated, density patterns in negative areas near the perforations can occur. When sheet film being processed in hangers is agitated too vigorously, developer streaming through holes in the hanger can cause "streaks" of increased density. Again, the prevention is proper agitation.

While development uniformity is desirable with all films, KODAK Technical Pan Film is more sensitive to developing nonuniformity, so special care must be taken. See page 60. When the sheet form of KODAK Technical Pan Film is being used for continuous-tone work, tray development is more likely to produce uniform density than tank development.

Machine Processing

Roller transport processors generally provide very even development across the surfaces of both roll and sheet films. For those who have many films to process, they provide a fine way to process copy films. The amount of development for each type of film is adjusted by varying the speed of the processor film transport.

Densitometry for Copy Control

As with regular photography, much copying can be done with empirical controls and satisfactory results can be obtained. Judging negative densities and contrast by eye can be a reasonably accurate way to control copy negative quality.

However, when large numbers of copies are being made, or when the utmost copy quality is desired, a measurement control system can be of value. The measuring device used for this purpose is a densitometer.

Density: Density is a measure of the blackness, or light-absorbing characteristic of an area in a photograph. Transmission density is a measure of the light-absorbing characteristic of an area in a negative or a transparency. Reflection density is a measure of the light-absorbing characteristic of an area in a print.

When used to control the copying (or duplicating) process, transmission density (usually just called density) is used.

Technically, density is the logarithm to the base 10 of the opacity, which is the reciprocal of the transmittance.

$$D = Log_{10}\ 0 = Log_{10}\ \frac{1}{T}$$

If an area in a negative transmits half the light, it has a transmittance of 1/2, or 0.50. Thus:

$$Transmittance = \frac{Transmitted\ Light}{Incident\ Light}$$

where incident light is the light that falls on the film, and transmitted light is the light that passes through the film.

The percent transmission is 100 times the transmittance. If only half the light is transmitted, there is a transmittance of 0.50, or a 50 percent transmission.

Opacity is the reciprocal of the transmittance.

$$Opacity = \frac{1}{Transmittance} \quad or \quad \frac{Incident\ Light}{Transmitted\ Light}$$

A film area that has a transmittance of 0.50 has an opacity of 1/0.50 = 2.00.

Density is the logarithm of the opacity; an area of film that has an opacity of 2.00 has a density of 0.301.

$$Log_{10}\ \frac{1}{0.50} = \quad Log_{10}\ 2.00 = \quad 0.301$$

The following table shows transmittance, opacity, and density values of a few useful negative or transparency values.

Transmittance	Opacity	Density
1.000	1.000	0.000
.977	1.023	0.010
.891	1.122	0.050
.794	1.259	0.100
.500	2.000	0.301
.316	3.162	.500
.100	10.	1.000
.010	100.	2.000
.001	1,000.	3.000

The incident light generally used in densitometry is diffuse light, so technically in the following discussion densities are diffuse transmission densities.

Fortunately, densitometers are calibrated directly in density units so that it is not necessary to calculate densities from transmittances. These relationships are given to show that densities are valuable in determining how much light goes through a negative area with a measurable density value. It is the varying amounts of light going through the negative areas that expose the photographic paper to make the copy print.

Log Lux Second (steps at 1.0 log lx sec)	3̄.0	2̄.0	1̄.0	0.0	1.0	2.0	3.0
Lux Second	0.001	0.01	0.1	1.0	10	100	1000

Log Lux Second (steps at 0.2 log lx sec)	3̄.0	3̄.2	3̄.4	3̄.6	3.8	2.0
Lux Second	0.0010	0.0016	0.0025	0.0040	0.0063	0.0100

Characteristic Curves (H&D Curves, or D-Log E Curves): When a film is exposed to varying amounts of light and is developed, various densities result. If known exposures are given, and the resultant densities plotted against the exposures, a characteristic curve results.

Exposure values are given in lux seconds. A lux is a meter candle—that is, the illuminance falling on a surface that is 1 meter from a standard candle. Exposure is illuminance X time (E = IT), and since time is calibrated in seconds, exposure values are lux seconds. Because density values are logarithmic, log lux-second values are used as the base units.

When a film is developed, the various amounts of densities have resulted from various amounts of exposure. If each density is plotted on graph paper directly above the log exposure value that produced it, a series of points results. When these points are connected with a smooth curved line, the characteristic curve of that particular film developed in a particular way is produced.

Three characteristic curves are shown on this page. The first is of a typical black-and-white camera film. Notice that the log exposure units on the scale are both in whole numbers and in bar values. Bar logs are minus logs, and represent decimal parts of 1 lux second exposure. The characteristics only are minus, the mantissas remain positive. The table on the top of the page shows the relationship between the log exposure values and the exposure values.

In the first curve illustrated, the toe section and the straight line portion of the curve are shown. In the toe section, the dark tones are recorded. Dark tones are compressed—that is, the separation between the tones is less than it is on the straight line. For copying purposes, it is wise to copy so that the darkest tone is reproduced just above the toe so that all tones are reproduced on the straight line. To accomplish this, a negative must be overexposed moderately. In this case, the compression of tones is only caused by the paper curve shape.

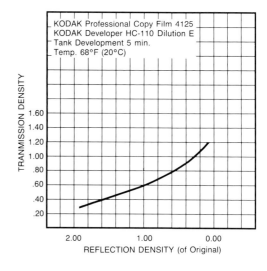

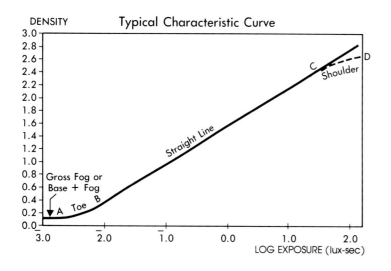

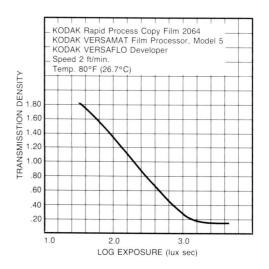

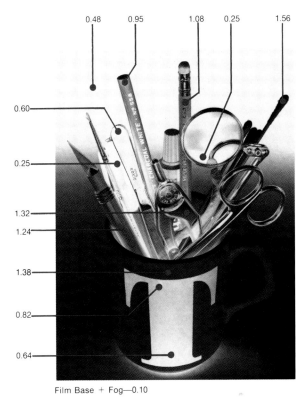

0.48 0.95 1.08 0.25 1.56

0.60

0.25

1.32

1.24

1.38

0.82

0.64

Film Base + Fog—0.10

The resultant negative densities are controlled by the subject illumination and reflectance, the camera exposure, the film, and the development. These factors are controlled by the photographer to obtain negatives with densities that will produce prints with good quality.

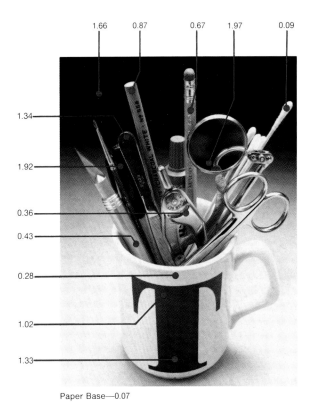

1.66 0.87 0.67 1.97 0.09

1.34

1.92

0.36

0.43

0.28

1.02

1.33

Paper Base—0.07

The print reflection densities are controlled by the negative densities, the type of enlarger, the paper, the print exposure, and the print development.

The second curve shows the characteristics of KODAK Professional Copy Film. The use of this film was discussed earlier in the section "Tone Reproduction in Copying." The upsweep in the curve where the original highlights are reproduced gives increased separation to the original light tones in the copy negative. This tends to compensate for the highlight compression of tones caused by the printing paper on which the copy negative will be printed.

The third characteristic curve is of 35mm direct duplicating film, KODAK Rapid Process Copy Film 2064. The dark tones are produced by the least exposure, while the light tones are the result of more exposure. The curve slopes in the opposite direction from that of negative films. While designed as a duplicating film, this film can be used to copy prints, thus making blue-based slides in one step. Processing recommendations are given in the data sheet packaged with the film. Since this film is blue-sensitive, it is generally suitable for copying black-and-white originals only. As indicated by the curve position on the log exposure scale, this is a very slow film.

Density Range: The density range of a copy negative is the difference between the density of the original white paper highlights, which are darkest in the negative, and the density of the deepest original black, which is the lightest area of the negative. Since most copy negatives are moderately overexposed to get the

dark tones up off the toe of the characteristic curve, the lightest area in the image of the negative should have a greater density than the film base.

Density range is useful in determining the printing characteristics of negatives.

Black-and-white negatives with a density range of about 1.05 usually print well on normal grade papers with diffusion enlargers. For condenser enlargers, a lower density range, usually about 0.85, is required. However, with KODAK Technical Pan Film, the 1.05 value works well with both types of enlargers. The grain is so fine that there is little Callier effect, i.e., increase in contrast when enlarging due to light scattering.

When black-and-white KODAK films such as PLUS-X Pan, Commercial, EKTAPAN, T-MAX, and Technical Pan are used for copying, the main control of density range is by the amount of development, or the developer type. Usually the developing time is increased over the standard recommendations given on the instruction sheets packaged with the films because typical real-life subjects have greater luminance ranges than the original photographs or artwork normally copied.

As previously mentioned, with KODAK Professional Copy Film, the density range is controlled primarily by exposure. Increasing the exposure places more of the picture tones on the upsweep part of the characteristic curve where the highlight densities increase more rapidly than the shadow densities, giving a greater density range.

When an original print has high quality, and a proper exposure is given on a special copy film, a high-quality copy negative results.

The print from which this illustration was made is a copy print of the print above. The copy negative was made on KODAK Professional Copy Film exposed to give added contrast in the highlights. It is difficult to distinguish the original print from the copy print.

This series of three illustrations illustrates the difference in contrast between different prints. This is a high-contrast print with a density range of 1.60.

This is a normal contrast print. The text gives two methods of exposing copy negatives of prints with different contrasts. The density range of the original print is 1.31.

This is a low-contrast print. When using KODAK Professional Copy Film, the recommended method is to expose all copy negatives to obtain a constant highlight density. The use of different grades of photographic paper gives the copy print contrast desired. The density range of this print is 1.13.

Reflection Densities: Originals that are copied are not all alike in their luminance ranges. This is caused by variations in their reflection densities. Reflection density is similar to transmission density except that the basic value is reflectance instead of transmittance. Absorptance is the reciprocal of the reflectance. Reflection density is the logarithm to the base 10 of the absorptance.

$$\text{Absorptance} = \frac{1}{\text{Reflectance}} \quad \text{or} \quad \frac{\text{Incident light}}{\text{Reflected light}}$$

$$\text{Reflection density} = \text{Log}_{10}\ \text{absorptance}$$

Reflection density is measured with reflection densitometers. These are calibrated to read reflection densities directly. Color densitometers have a setting with which black-and-white reflection densities can be measured.

If the color settings are marked red, green, and blue, the black-and-white setting is likely to be marked amber. If the color settings are marked cyan, magenta, and yellow, the black-and-white setting is likely to be marked black. The use of this setting will give the appropriate black-and-white density measurements.

However, if the original print being copied is faded to a yellowish color and is being copied with a blue filter, or with a blue-sensitive film, it is better to measure the reflection density range with the blue filter in position in the densitometer. This position may be labeled blue or yellow, depending on the particular densitometer.

When high-quality copying is being done using regular films and the copy negatives are being individually processed, the reflection density range of the originals can be used to determine the developing time to obtain consistent negative density ranges. For example, if a print has a reflection density range of 2.0, and a developing time is found that gives a negative density range of 1.05, prints with less reflection density range should receive a longer developing time to achieve the same negative density range of 1.05. A series of experiments with your own equipment and materials will indicate how much change in developing time is needed for a given change in reflection density range.

When using KODAK Professional Copy Film, it is important to place the light to white tones on the same place on the characteristic curve shape of the copy film (and to maintain the same development). Each copy negative is given the same exposure, adjusting only for lens extension and darker-than-normal "whites" in the original. Negative density range will vary, and adjustment for negative density range is made in the choice of paper contrast when printing.

DENSITOMETERS

Both transmission and reflection densities are measured with instruments called densitometers.

Optical densitometers use a visual comparison method to measure density. Electronic densitometers use some type of light-sensitive device (cells, diodes) to measure densities and range in price from several hundred dollars to thousands. The more costly ones are likely to have a higher degree of these attributes: repeatability, spectral integrity, linear response, dynamic range, and low noise-to-signal ratio. Constant calibration and frequent maintenance are required for consistent, accurate measurements.

Densitometers that measure just black-and-white densities are less costly, but color densitometers are more versatile. If the possibility exists that color copying or duplicating may be done, it is probably a good investment to start right out with a color densitometer.

The ESECO Compumaster TQC color transmission and reflection densitometer includes automatic KODAK Q-LAB diagnostics. It also features 21-step internegative balancing with calculations. With a modem, data can be sent to labs in other locations.

As explained in the text, densitometry can be of aid in achieving high-quality results in copying and in duplicating, in both black and white and color. The Macbeth TR 1224 densitometer has a patented dual-head reading arm which contains two individual optical systems. Photo courtesy of Macbeth, division of Kollmorgen Instruments.

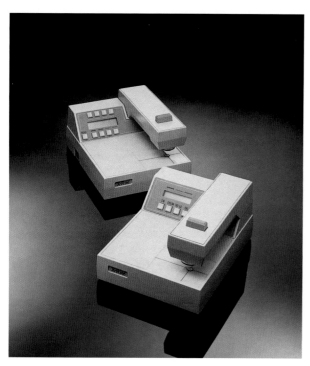

The X-Rite model 811TR and 820TR densitometers measure Status A transmission and reflection as well as Status M for negative film. The model 820TR also has a memory feature for easy process monitoring and internegative color balancing.

Special Techniques

USING FILTERS

Filters are used in a number of ways in black-and-white copying. Contrast filters, polarizing filters, and one type of specialized filter (diffusion) are used in this type of work. Only occasionally are conversion, light-balancing, and color compensating filters used except for color copying and duplicating.

CONTRAST FILTERS

The color filter circle on page 35 shows the various KODAK WRATTEN Filter numbers of the filters usually considered to be contrast filters. Contrast filters are strongly colored filters used to change the tonal rendition of colors when photographed in black and white.

As the color filter circle shows, colors that are similar to the filter being used are made lighter in the final print, while complementary colors, that is, those that are opposite on the circle, are darkened. When a red filter is used, reds, magentas, and yellows are lightened while blue-greens (cyans), blues, and greens are darkened.

Filters alter the balance of the wavelengths of light entering the camera. A red filter, such as the KODAK WRATTEN Filter No. 25, absorbs most of the blue and green light and transmits much of the red light. The film is only exposed to the red light. In order to expose the film properly, the exposure (shutter speed and/or aperture) must be increased. How much it is increased is determined by the filter factor. The filter factor for the No. 25 filter is 8X with daylight-balanced light and 5X with tungsten-balanced light with most panchromatic films.

The Color Filter Circle shows the filter factors for a variety of filters. One way to increase the exposure is to multiply the exposure time (shutter speed) by the filter factor. If the exposure time without a filter is 1/4 second, and the filter factor is 5X, the time (at the same f-number) is 5 x 1/4 = 5/4 = 1 1/4 = 1.25 seconds (for most applications, 1 second would be close enough).

Another way to increase the exposure is to open up the lens, that is, to change the f-number to a lower number. For example, if the filter factor is 5X, the increase in stops is 2 1/3. If the original aperture is f/16, the aperture corrected for the filter factor would be about f/7, or 1/3 stop larger than f/8. The following table gives the exposure change in stops for a variety of filter factors.

Filter Factor	+ Stops	Filter Factor	+ Stops	Filter Factors	+ Stops
1.25X	+ 1/3	4X	+ 2	12X	+ 3²/₃
1.5X	+ 2/3	5X	+ 2¹/₃	40X	+ 5¹/₃
2X	+ 1	6X	+ 2²/₃	100X	+ 6²/₃
2.5X	+ 1¹/₃	8X	+ 3	1000X	+ 10
3X	+ 1²/₃	10X	+ 3¹/₃		

For example, if the filter factor is 5X, the increase in stops is 2 1/3. If the original aperture is f/16, the aperture corrected for the filter factor would be about f/7, or 1/3 stop larger than f/8.

Uses of Contrast Filters: An important use of contrast filters is to eliminate or reduce the effects of a colored stain on the original. If an original black-and-white photograph has a red stain on it, and if it is copied through a red (No. 25 or 29) filter onto a panchromatic film, the copy negative will show a decided lightening of the stain effect. The copy print may even show no evidence of the stain.

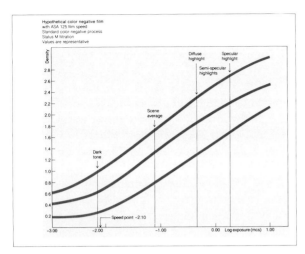

This colored graph serves as an example for the use of contrast filters.

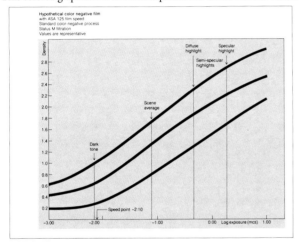

When copied without filtration on panchromatic film, the yellow background shows a light gray tint.

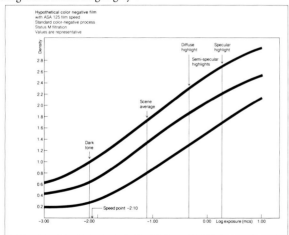

Using a KODAK WRATTEN Filter No. 8 (green) with a high-contrast panchromatic copy film eliminates the yellow and darkens the red. This then becomes a clean black-and-white line rendition of the colored graph.

The most common stain color is brown. The red filters mentioned above (Nos. 25 and 29) are the best to use to minimize brown stains. If the print is overall brown, a blue filter is used to enhance contrast.

Another use of contrast filters is to provide contrast between colors in an original when making black-and-white copies with panchromatic films. Two areas in the original may be separated well by color but may photograph as the same tone. By choosing a filter that lightens one color and darkens the other, the same areas will be separated by tone in the copy.

A third use of filters is to enhance the contrast in old, faded, brown-imaged prints. A deep blue filter (No. 47, 47B) increases the image contrast. This use is shown in the series illustrating the use of KODAK Technical Pan Film for copying on page 57. (For local brown stains, a red filter is used.)

Neutral Density, Conversion, Light-Balancing, and Color Compensating Filters: These filters are primarily used in color copying and duplicating and are rarely used in black-and-white copying. However, the use of a light-colored filter may be desirable, especially when copying colored originals on black-and-white film.

If two colored areas do not separate in tone when copying without a filter, and separate too much with the strongly colored contrast filters, the lighter colored filters, such as CC (color compensating) filters are useful. If, for example, the No. 25 red filter gives too much tone separation, a CC50R filter may provide the desired moderate tone separation. The bluish 80 series and orangish 85 series of conversion filters can be used in a like manner.

In rare instances, neutral density filters are used to provide longer copy exposure times with black-and-white (as well as color) copying. Longer exposure times may be needed if color film is balanced for long exposure times. In any copying, it is difficult to give exact exposure times of 1 1/2 seconds, for example. A 0.3 neutral density filter reduces the light reaching the film by a factor of 2. If you want to give the 1 1/2-second exposure without changing the f-number, place a 0.3 neutral density filter over the lens and expose for 3 seconds. The time error will be reduced. If the film requires it, an additional amount of time may be needed to correct for reciprocity law failure.

The illustration above is made from a copy of a daguerreotype. Daguerreotypes are shiny metallic silver images and require a special arrangement to copy.

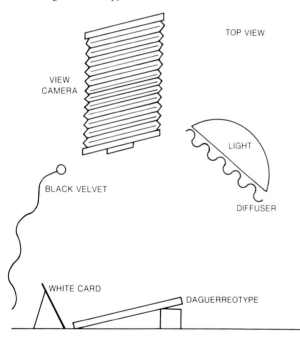

TOP VIEW

VIEW CAMERA

LIGHT

BLACK VELVET

DIFFUSER

WHITE CARD

DAGUERREOTYPE

Photographing a Daguerreotype with a View Camera
A diffuse light is placed to illuminate the daguerreotype, which is placed at an angle to the camera axis. A black velvet cloth is placed so that its black image reflects to the camera. A small white reflector is placed to reflect light across the daguerreotype. The camera front and back are tilted at the same angle as the daguerreotype to keep the image rectilinear.

COPYING DAGUERREOTYPES

A daguerreotype is a photographic image on a silver-coated copper plate, resulting in a mirror-like surface. To obtain a positive image, the daguerreotype must be reflecting a black surface to the camera. The diagram shows an arrangement that will reflect black

to the lens while the diffuse light tones are illuminated. The camera tilts correct for the distortion resulting from the angle of the daguerreotype.

COPYING WITH IR AND UV RADIATION

Infrared Copying: Infrared radiation is similar to visible light but occurs at slightly longer wavelengths. KODAK High Speed Infrared Film 4143 (ESTAR Thick Base) in sheets and its 35mm equivalent, KODAK High Speed Infrared Film 2481, have an infrared sensitivity to wavelengths from about 700 to 900 nanometers. (The eye is sensitive from about 400 to about 700 nanometers.) The film is also sensitive to blue light, so it is usually exposed through a red filter such as KODAK WRATTEN Filters No. 87, 25, 29, or 70, or in extreme cases, an infrared filter, No. 87C, if a record is required in the infrared region only.

As a result of its unusual sensitivity, infrared film "sees" differently than the eye and can be used to detect some things that cannot be seen. One use is to copy paintings where there is a suspicion that there is a painting under that which can be seen. The film may be able to see through the upper painting and show the under-painting—or at least show that there is an under-painting. This method does not work in all cases, but it is one of the methods to try if alterations in a painting are suspected.

Another important use of IR-sensitive film is to copy charred or burnt documents where the original writing is invisible. The original writing may be made visible in the infrared copy. Writing made illegible by age, by accumulation of dirt, by a stamp applied by a censor, by chemical bleaching, or by mechanical erasure may also be made visible in an infrared copy. Some inks fluoresce in the infrared region when stimulated with ultraviolet radiation. An infrared copy can make this fluorescence visible.

Filters and Light Sources for Infrared Copying: As indicated above, the No. 87 filter is commonly used for infrared copying. Incandescent bulbs are a good source of infrared radiation for copying. The exposure index when exposing with the No. 87 filter in incandescent light is 64, with the No. 87C filter, it is 25.

Sunlight contains infrared radiation and can be used as a light source for infrared copying. Electronic flash units also emit infrared radiation—low-voltage models emit a higher percentage of IR than do high-voltage models.

Testing for individual IR output levels for different types of flash units is recommended. Testing for the exposure based on the IR output of a flash generally follows the same procedures used for testing a flash's GN (Guide Number). That is, position the subject at a specific distance with the flash set on manual, full power. Look at the light output scale of the flash unit and select the appropriate aperture for an ISO that is close to the suggested "daylight" ISO of the infrared film. Now make a series of under- and over exposures in 1/2-stop increments using the aperture dial of the lens. It is a good idea to set the subject at a distance that permits the "correct" beginning exposure to be at the midpoint on the aperture scale giving a full range of under- and overexposure settings. The correctly exposed frame will then give both a GN and ISO setting for that flash and film combination.

Focusing for Infrared Copying: Most lenses used for copying are corrected to focus only visible light on the same plane. Infrared radiation focuses at a slightly longer lens-to-film distance. Therefore, visual focus will not give precise infrared focus. Some lenses have an indicator, usually a red mark, on the focusing scale for infrared focus. When using an IR filter, align the camera to subject distance with the IR indicator. When using red filters that transmit visible light as well as IR, set the focus distance part way between the IR and visible light focus indicators. With lenses not marked, as with view camera lenses, the procedure is to focus visually and then increase the lens-to-film distance by 0.25 percent. If the lens-to-film distance is 10 inches, for example, the increase required would be:

$$0.0025 \times 10 \text{ inches} = 0.025 \text{ inch}$$

.025 inch is slightly less than 1/32 inch. In most cases, stopping the lens down as is generally done when copying should provide enough depth of field to accommodate the difference in focal length between visible light and infrared radiation.

Infrared copy negatives may not be as sharp as their visual counterparts because the aberrations of the lens have been corrected for visible light and not infrared radiation. Stopping the lens down to moderately small apertures will minimize the effects of some of the aberrations and provide improved sharpness.

Infrared luminescence is generally caused by illuminating an object with blue-green light. Certain materials will then emit infrared radiation. While photographing IR luminescence is generally used in scientific photography of biological specimens and minerals, it is sometimes used in law enforcement photography. Filters or screens made of 9780 Corning Glass color filter, C.S. No. 4-76, molded, 8 mm (blue-green) are generally recommended, but a KODAK WRATTEN Filter No. 44 combined with a KODAK Infrared Cutoff Filter No. 301A can also be used. The 301A filter is placed nearest the light. An infrared filter such as the KODAK WRATTEN Filter No. 87 is placed over the camera lens. Exposure is based on experience gained by running an exposure series.

This check was copied on regular film with normal illumination. It looks perfectly normal.

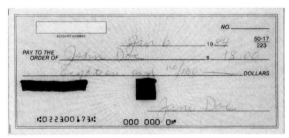

Copied with infrared radiation, it can easily be seen that the value of the check has been raised with a different ink than was originally used. Some trial and error with filters may be necessary. This copy was made on KODAK High Speed Infrared Film using KODAK WRATTEN Filter No. 89B.

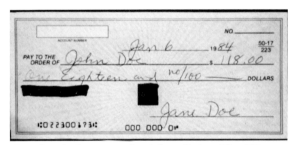

Copied with short wave ultraviolet radiation. The difference between the two inks in the copy is considerably less than with infrared. With other inks. UV copies might show up the difference better than IR copies. This copy was made on KODAK Technical Pan Film developed in KODAK D-19 Developer.

COPYING BY ULTRAVIOLET RADIATION

While infrared radiation has wavelengths longer than those of light, ultraviolet radiation has wavelengths shorter than those of light.

Ultraviolet copy photography has some of the same uses as infrared copying. It is often used in the study of paintings and to detect faded or vanished writing and chemical erasures. It is particularly useful in law enforcement photography to detect forgeries.

The wavelengths of the ultraviolet band of radiation extends from about 10 nanometers to 400 nanometers, where visible light starts. However, the glass in photographic lenses transmits beginning only from about 350 nm to 400 nm, so that this is the region commonly used in UV photography. All normal black-and-white films are sensitive through the entire UV band, so that no special films are required. As with infrared copying, one method is required for copying ultraviolet reflection, while the other is used for ultraviolet fluorescence.

Copying Infrared Reflectance

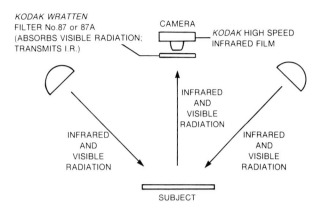

The basic setup for reflectance infrared copying. Tungsten lamps are a good source of IR radiation.

Copying Ultraviolet Reflectance

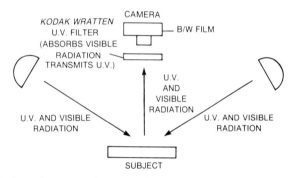

Lights rich in UV radiation, such as arc lights, fluorescent lights, or pulsed xenon lights are used for UV copying. The UV filter over the lens allows only UV to record on the film.

Copying Infrared Luminescence

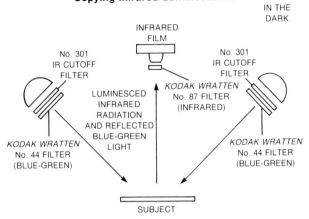

When copying luminescence caused by IR radiation, the subject is illuminated with blue-green light by using a No. 44 filter over each light. The camera lens is filtered with a No. 87 filter so only infrared radiation is transmitted to the lens. The copying is done in the dark.

Copying Ultraviolet Fluorescence

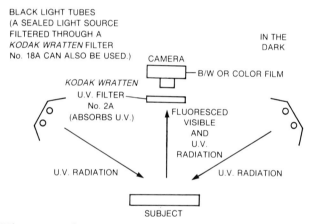

When copying luminescence caused by ultraviolet radiation, the subject is illuminated by ultraviolet radiation and no light. A filter that absorbs UV is placed over the lens. The fluorescence is in wavelengths of light and is photographed with a regular black-and-white or color film.

Ultraviolet Reflection Copying: This is the primary method used in copying to detect forgeries. In this method, the copy is illuminated with any light source that contains ultraviolet radiation, and a filter is placed over the lens that transmits only ultraviolet radiation. An alternative method is to illuminate the copy with a source that emits only ultraviolet radiation, and to copy with no filter over the lens. This must be done in total darkness.

The black lights sold for special visual effects with fluorescent posters can be used for casual UV copying but may not be suitable for critical use. A General Electric UVIARC or other UV source can be fitted into a lighttight box equipped with a suitable UV filter to emit ultraviolet radiation only.

Ultraviolet Fluorescence Copying: Certain materials absorb ultraviolet radiation and emit light—they fluoresce. For copying this fluorescence, the copy must be illuminated by ultraviolet radiation only, and the copying must be done in the dark. Such UV sources are described above.

A filter that absorbs ultraviolet radiation is used over the camera lens so that only the fluoresced light is copied. Such filters include the KODAK WRATTEN

Filters No. 2A, 2B, and 2E. Some inks tend to fluoresce under UV stimulation. This method should be tried when the writing on a document has faded badly. It may fluoresce, giving a better copy image of the writing. A high-contrast film such as KODAK Contrast Process Ortho Film 4154 (ESTAR Thick Base) or KODAK Technical Pan Film 2415 are recommended for this type of photography.

Color film can be used to copy the fluorescence of posters printed with fluorescent printing inks, as well as the fluorescence of certain minerals.

No focusing correction is usually required for ultraviolet copying, but small apertures are recommended for minimizing aberrations and providing enough depth of field to compensate for a slight focus shift between visible and UV focus. Fairly long exposure times on the order of 1 minute at $f/16$ are required.

USING POLARIZING FILTERS

The use of polarizing filters* is a valuable technique in copying. The main purpose for polarizing filters is to control reflections which in turn increases color saturation in color copying and often increases contrast.

Polarizing filters work by taking advantage of the wave nature of light. Unpolarized light vibrates in all directions, with the direction of the wave vibration being perpendicular to the direction of the path of light in all planes. Polarized light vibrates in only one direction. It occurs when light is reflected at an oblique angle off polished, non-metallic surfaces such as those of glass, water, glossy photographs, or shiny painted surfaces.

Polarization also occurs when light passes through a polarizing filter. Because the light reflecting from a shiny surface at oblique angles vibrates in one direction, a polarizing filter can block that light by only allowing light to pass that vibrates in a different direction. The first two illustrations show how unpolarized light is polarized by a shiny surface and by a polarizing filter. The third drawing illustrates how a polarizing filter eliminates a reflection.

Originals that are not shiny-surfaced will not fully polarize the light as it is reflected. With such originals it is helpful to have polarizing screens over the light sources. Maximum polarization, however, is obtained by using polarizing screens over the lights and a polarizing filter over the camera lens. This technique is called double or crossed polarization. A schematic of this technique is illustrated on page 54.

*We have observed the convention that polarizing filters are used over the camera lens, and polarizing screens are used over the lights although the polarizing material is the same.

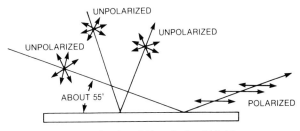

Polarized and Unpolarized Light

The diagram shows the angle of maximum polarization from a plate glass surface. The angle with a water surface is about 47°.

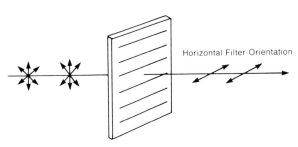

Polarizing Filter

The light beam coming in from the left is unpolarized light and the light waves vibrate in all directions at 90° to the beam path. After going through the polarizer, the light waves vibrate in only one direction, in the drawing, horizontally. A horizontal sheet of glass polarizes the light horizontally.

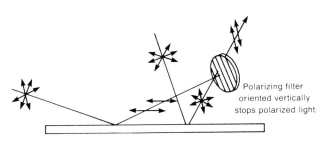

Eliminating a Reflection

If a polarizing filter is placed over the lens with its polarization vertical, the reflected polarized light is absorbed, effectively eliminating the reflection.

A word of caution when working with polarizing filters. There are two types of polarizing filters available, linear and circular, and using the correct type is critical. Modern SLR autofocus, auto-exposure cameras employ beam-splitters within the light's pathway to divide the amount of light between what is seen in the viewfinder and what is used by the autofocus and auto-exposure mechanisms. Commonly, this is a 3:1 ratio, but if a linear polarizing filter is employed, the total amount of light will decrease and the ratio will be changed to different degrees depending on how much of its polarizing function is being employed. The result can be incorrect exposures.

A circular polarizer, while also cutting down on the total amount of light that is being passed as part of its polarizing function, will not affect the ratio of light being produced by the beam-splitter and generally give correct readings. If there is no beam-splitter mechanism involved in the camera's viewing and exposure system, then either type of polarizer can be used.

Adjusting polarizers is relatively simple. When a polarizing filter is used over the lens only, the filter is rotated until the image on the camera ground glass or viewfinder in a single-lens-reflex camera shows the least amount of reflection. For cameras that do not have through-the-lens viewing systems, the adjustment can be made by viewing the copy from the camera's vantage point and rotating the filter in front of the eye until the reflections are minimized. The position of the filter is noted, and it is then placed on the camera lens with the same orientation.

In a vertical copy setup when polarizing screens are used over the lights only, the maximum effect is gained by orienting the polarizing screens so that they polarize horizontally. In a horizontal copy setup the maximum effect would be gained by orienting the screens to polarize vertically. The orientation of the screen refers to the direction in which light must vibrate in order to be able to pass through the screen. To determine the vertical orientation of a screen, look at a reflection from a horizontal surface through the screen. Rotate the polarizing screen until the reflection is eliminated. This is the vertical orientation of the screen. Rotate the screen ninety degrees to put the screen in horizontal orientation. Label the screen at the top for its polarization direction for future reference. The screens should be placed in the proper orientation in front of the lights before shooting.

When double polarization is used for maximum reflection control, the polarizing screens on the light sources should be oriented first (one at a time), then the polarizing filter on the lens can be rotated until the reflection is minimized. The procedure can be reversed, adjusting the polarizing filter on the lens first. A shiny coin placed on the copyboard helps to detect the effects of the polarizers.

When artwork that has a transparent overlay, such as an animation cel, is copied with polarizing filters, stress patterns from the overlay material may appear in the copy. To avoid this effect, acetate cels should be used for the artwork or polarizers should not be used.

Polarization is often essential for the highest quality copy work. There are many situations in which polarizing provides the difference between an unacceptable copy and a copy of high quality. Polarization is helpful for eliminating "silvering" when copying old photographic prints. It helps eliminate or minimize the texture of rough-surfaced prints. When transparent or translucent tape has been used on the surface of a print to repair a tear (a destructive practice) polarization can make the tape almost invisible in the copy. Polarization is also extremely helpful when copying paintings. Illustrations showing applications of polarization are on page 55.

Whenever polarizing filters are used, an exposure compensation must be made (unless a through-the-lens meter is used). Most polarizing filters have a fil-

Lights with polarizing screens are used when double or crossed polarization is needed to eliminate specular reflections.

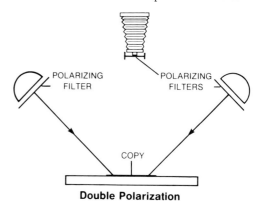

Double Polarization

Copying lights are often at angles to the copy surface other than the angle of maximum polarization. Putting polarizing screens over the lights and a polarizing filter over the lens can eliminate reflections. The text explains how to orient the polarizers.

ter factor of 2.5X to 3.0X and require an exposure increase of about 1 1/2 *f*-stops. When polarizing screens are used over the lights, an additional increase in exposure is necessary. This increase can be measured by taking a light meter reading with the screens over the lights and comparing it to a reading without the screens over the lights*. The difference in measured exposure should be added to the tested basic exposure in use. The exposure required with crossed polarization may be 20 times the exposure without the polarizers. It may also be necessary to include an increase for the reciprocity characteristics of the film when exposure times get long.

An increase in color saturation may also be noticed as a result of polarization. This is because the polarization filter removes specular reflections from the image which would otherwise dilute the colors. At the same time, the contrast of the copy image is increased because the specular reflection would otherwise lower the contrast. This increased image contrast helps increase shadow tone separation in the copy. With single-lens-reflex cameras that have beam-splitting mirrors, these effects may not occur, or may occur but with incorrect exposure. Circular polarizers are available for such cameras.

*This does not work with cameras that have beam-splitters in the optical path.

Some old photographs "silver-out" or develop a mirror-like silver surface in certain high-density areas. Note the loss of blacks, especially in the lower part of the picture in this copy photograph made with unpolarized light.

If copied with double polarization, the effects of the silvering-out are minimized in the copy.

Another use of polarizers is to minimize texture in copying prints made on a textured paper. This print was copied without polarizers.

The same print was copied using double polarization. The texture on the original print has been reduced in the copy.

Polarizing filters that are used in front of camera lenses are easily obtained in camera stores or from other photographic suppliers. Polarizing filters (screens) that are used in front of lights must be large enough to span the width of the front of the light. For this, large sheets of polarizing filter material are necessary and are sometimes difficult to get. One company that sells large sheets of polarizing material is Edmund Scientific Company in Barrington, NJ.

COPYING YELLOWED AND FADED ORIGINALS WITH KODAK TECHNICAL PAN FILM 2415

Possibly one of the most perplexing problems in copying yellowed and faded photographs, especially for the inexperienced, is the choice of film, filter, and developer. Usually a considerable amount of time, in trial and error experimentation, is required.

A very versatile film, KODAK Technical Pan Film 2415 makes this an easier and more pleasant task. The film has extremely fine grain, extremely high resolution, and uncommon flexibility in processing. The fine-grain characteristic of this film makes it ideal for copying medium- to low-contrast originals with 35mm, medium-format, and 4 x 5-inch-format cameras. Developed in KODAK Developer D-19 or KODAK DEKTOL Developer, it can be used to copy high-contrast originals like pen and ink drawings. With a concentrated developer such as KODAK HC-110 Developer, it is possible to use a range of developer dilutions to accommodate originals with varying density ranges.

In the illustrations on the following pages, originals were selected that had various density ranges. They represent photographs in progressive degrees of fading, from prints that are almost normal to severely faded and yellowed specimens. A negative was made from each of the originals that had good printing characteristics. Each of the reproductions made from the negatives showed an improvement in tone rendition over the original.

The chart shows how the different originals were handled with two developer dilutions using KODAK HC-110 Developer. Variable-contrast, resin-coated paper with variable-contrast printing filters was used to make the prints. The originals that were extremely yellowed required the use of a KODAK WRATTEN Filter No. 47 (blue) over the camera lens. The developing time was 8 minutes for all the films in both of the dilutions. This developing time is a starting point and should be used as a guide only.

KODAK Technical Pan Film 2415 also has extended red sensitivity. Technical Pan Film without the use of any filters will record the reddish areas so that they are slightly lighter than normal in the print. If it is not desirable to lighten the reddish areas, a KODAK WRATTEN Filter No. 38 or a KODAK Color Compensating Filter CC40C may be used to neutralize the extended red sensitivity of the film. A filter factor of 1.5X can be used for the CC40C filter while a filter factor of 2X in tungsten and 4X in daylight must be used for the No. 38 filter. It may be helpful to do this when copying color prints, hand-colored photographs, or warm-toned prints.

Some old deteriorated photographs may have reddish patches or spots. Commonly, when reddish patches or spots occur, they are stains. It is usually desirable to eliminate or minimize the tone of the stain. The extended red sensitivity of Technical Pan Film is an advantage in this case. Used in conjunction with a red filter, such as a KODAK WRATTEN Filter No. 25, it is a very effective tool for minimizing reddish stains. However, if a red or reddish brown spot occurs in a dense area, it may be due to oxidation and should not be lightened by the use of a red filter. Copy with no filter or with a CC40C filter.

Filter factors for these filters and others are given on the next page. These filter factors only apply to KODAK Technical Pan Film because of its extended red sensitivity.

Original	Filter	Developer Dilution	KODAK POLYCONTRAST Printing Filter	Density Range of Original
#1	—	HC-110F	1	1.12
#2	—	HC-110F	2	1.05
#3	47B	HC-110B	2½	.99
#4	47B	HC-110B	3	.94
#5	47B	HC-110B	3½	.61
#6	47B	HC-110B	3½	.50

Set 1. In this series, KODAK Technical Pan Film developed in KODAK HC-110 Developer is used to compensate for variations in original print contrast. This print is only slightly faded and is copied in a manner similar to copying regular prints.

The copy print has close to the same tonal characteristics as the original print. See the table opposite for filter and developing data.

Set 2. This print has slightly less contrast than the first original. Exposure and processing were the same, however, and the contrast gain was achieved in printing.

The copy print has been brought back to a normal contrast. If a brown color is desirable, the copy prints can be toned.

Because of the extremely fine grain and high resolving power of this film, it is a valuable film for copying with small-format cameras. When copying with roll film, group originals together according to contrast so that low-contrast originals are shot on one roll of film, normal-contrast originals on another, etc. Then the roll that contains the low-contrast originals can be developed longer (or in a stronger developer dilution), the roll that contains normal originals can be developed for the normal time, etc. Using the example provided above, it is possible to group the originals into two categories for copying so that only two rolls of film would be necessary: the extremely low-contrast originals requiring a strong developer (i.e., less dilute) and originals that are near normal in contrast requiring a more dilute developer. Contrast refinements can be made for negatives within these groups during printing by using appropriate paper grades or KODAK POLYCONTRAST Filters (with KODAK POLYMAX Fiber Paper or KODAK POLYMAX Fine-Art Paper).

| KODAK WRATTEN Filter | Filter Factors | |
	Tungsten	Daylight
No. 8	1.2X	1.5X
No. 25	2 X	3 X
No. 38	2 X	3 X
No. 47	25 X	12 X

Set 3. The contrast of this print has been reduced considerably by the effects of time and fumes in the air. Perhaps it was not washed adequately when it was made.

Because of the strong brown color, a blue filter was used to copy this print, and a stronger developing solution was used to develop the copy negative.

Set 4. The contrast of this print is lower yet, probably due to the effects of time and fumes. In this print, the highlights have stained, lowering the reflection density range.

This print was copied the same as set 3 but printed with more contrast. Because the highlights have been raised in tone and the dark tones deepened, a normal tonal range has been restored.

Set 5. The same things have happened to this original as happened to the set 4 original, only more so. While the image is discernible, the print has a very low contrast.

The copy print has brought back the contrast, but the shadow detail has been nearly lost. (It may not have been in the print originally.)

Set 6. This print has browned and faded so badly that the image is very difficult to make out. However, the flexibility of this method of copying is useful, even with this type of original.

By using the blue filter, a full development, and by printing with a high-contrast POLYCONTRAST Filter, the image in the copy print has been made quite visible.

An alternative to using KODAK Technical Pan Film when copying low-contrast originals is to use KODAK Process Ortho Film.

This copy print was made with normal-contrast paper.

Developing KODAK Technical Pan Film: Small- and medium-format Technical Pan Film can be developed in a tank on spiral metal or plastic reels. As illustrated, KODAK TECHNIDOL Liquid Developer requires certain agitation techniques.

1. Before loading the film on the reels, fill the developing tank with the amount of developer needed to fill the tank. Leave enough space at the top to allow for later insertion of the loaded reel without overflowing.

2. After the reels are loaded, place the loaded reels smoothly and quickly into the tank filled as above with developer.

3. Replace the top on the developer tank. Tap the tank once or twice on a hard surface to dislodge air bells from the surface of the film.

4. Agitate for 2 seconds with "paint can" shake described in illustration.

5. Let the tank sit for the remainder of the first 30 seconds.

6. At intervals of 30 seconds for the rest of the development, agitate for 2 seconds using "paint can" shake.

Agitation Technique for TECHNIDOL Liquid Developer
Rapidly shake tank up and down over a distance of a few inches as if you were shaking a paint can. Do not rotate the tank.

Agitation may vary from individual to individual depending upon that person's technique and depending upon the amount of contrast desired. More agitation will produce more contrast; less agitation will produce less contrast.

Overagitation, particularly during the first minute of development, can cause uneven development. Often, the uneven development is characterized by areas of extra density near the sprocket holes of the film. Insufficient agitation during the first minute of development will cause uneven development or mottle over the entire surface of the film.

Large-format Technical Pan Film should be processed in a tray for best results. Development of Technical Pan Film in sheet film hangers tends to produce unacceptable unevenness of development. Developing times shorter than five minutes should be avoided for both rolls and sheets of KODAK Technical Pan Film. It is difficult to develop sheets of Technical Pan Film to a contrast-index of 0.56 or lower without getting uneven densities.

IMPROVING HIGHLIGHT TONE RENDITION

As discussed earlier, one of the frequent tone-rendition occurrences in copying is the compression of highlight tones so that they look muddy, making the copy print lose sparkle. KODAK Professional Copy Film usually improves highlight tone rendition, but for several reasons there are instances where this cannot be used. It may not be available in a size to fit the copy camera, the originals may be in color so that a panchromatic film is needed, or only occasional copies are made and Professional Copy Film is not available at the time. Highlight rendition by conventional black-and-white films can be improved in several ways.

Chemical Method: The copy negative can be locally intensified in the highlight areas (densest areas in the negative). A single solution intensifier is applied locally to the negative in the highlight areas, increasing the density and contrast in these areas. A cotton swab or spotting brush can be used to apply the intensifier. The gain in density can be controlled by placing the negative over an illuminator during the intensification. Selenium toner can also be used as a local intensifier for this purpose. The density-contrast increase with a particular toning is shown in the graph.

Dye Methods: The highlight areas of the copy negative can be increased in density by applying dyes such as KODAK Crocein Scarlet or neutral spotting dyes. The dye is applied locally using a cotton swab and spotting brushes. While increasing the effective negative density of the highlights, this method does not increase their contrast, as does the intensifier method.

Photographic Masking: The density and contrast of the copy negative highlight regions can be enhanced by use of a highlight mask.

A single-step masking procedure consists of contact-printing the negative onto a black-and-white direct duplicating film. KODAK Professional B/W Duplicating Film (ESTAR Thick Base) can be used. A relatively long exposure and long developing time is used to provide densities only in the highlight regions and to provide adequate contrast to the mask. When processed, the highlight mask is registered with the copy negative and taped into place.

The two-step method of making a highlight mask consists of making a contact positive transparency image first and then using this transparency to make a negative highlight mask.

Intensification with KODAK Selenium Toner

KODAK Technical Pan Film
Lower curve: untreated negative
Upper curve: KODAK Rapid Selenium Toner, 1:3, 7 minutes

DENSITY / RELATIVE LOG EXPOSURE

The graph illustrates the increase in density and contrast achieved by treating negatives with KODAK Rapid Selenium Toner. If the negative highlights in a copy negative are locally intensified by toning, the tonal separation lost in copying can be restored.

The positive can be made on film such as KODAK Commercial Film by the same procedures described in the section on making duplicate black-and-white negatives by the two-step process on page 123.

The highlight mask is made by contact printing the positive on a high-contrast film such as KODALITH Ortho Film, Type 3. Development can be in KODAK Developer D-11. Exposure should be just enough that only the highlights show in the mask, and the maximum density is about 0.25 to 0.50. When the highlight mask is registered and taped to the original negative, the highlight densities will appear enhanced.

If the highlights appear washed out in the copy print, the highlight mask densities are too great. If they still appear muddy, the highlight mask densities are not great enough.

A third technique is the in-camera method. The regular copy negative is exposed. Then a sheet of KODALITH Film is exposed lightly to record just the highlight areas. This in-camera mask is developed as above in KODAK Developer D-11. After both negatives are dry, they are registered. Obviously this requires a view camera on a rock-steady support.

Another method of restoring highlight contrast to copies is to use a highlight mask. This is a print from the original negative without masking.

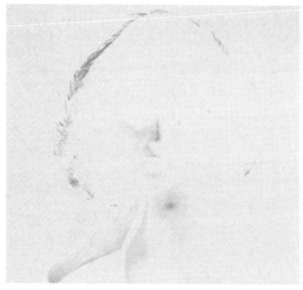

A highlight mask has densities only in the highlight areas. See the text for details on making these masks.

The mask is registered with the original negative, giving added density and contrast to the highlight areas. A print made from the masked negative shows the improvement in highlight tonal separation.

Using Diffusion Techniques

In most copying, every effort is made to retain the sharpness of the original in the copy print. However, there are situations where a slight degree of diffusion in the copy image becomes desirable.

When the final print is a copy restoration, there is often handwork on the intermediate print or on the copy negative. If the copy print is enlarged, a slight degree of diffusion minimizes the chances of the handwork showing.

Copying may be used to transform a snapshot of a person into a portrait-type photograph. Diffusion can change the image characteristics in such a way as to enhance the facial portrayal.

If the original is on a textured paper, and the usual methods of reducing the reproduction of the texture are only partially successful, diffusion of the copy image can reduce the visibility of the texture in the copy print.

These methods can be used successfully to diffuse the images:

1. Use of a soft-focus portrait lens for copying.
2. Use of commercially available diffusion filters or fog filters.
3. Use of homemade diffusion filters.

Following are some pointers about diffusing.

- Soft-focus portrait lenses usually provide variable amounts of diffusion, depending on the aperture used. Stopped down, such lenses usually provide sharper images; wide open, they provide a maximum amount of diffusion; at intermediate apertures, various intermediate degrees of diffusion are provided.

- The copy negative is made in the usual way, using the portrait lens as the copy lens. Initially several copy negatives can be made at different apertures to find the degree of diffusion that works best. With experience, the proper aperture can be selected directly.

- Commercially made diffusion filters (or discs) are available from a number of sources. They are made in different degrees of diffusion. Changing the aperture provides an additional control on the degree of diffusion.

- With normal diffusion filters, a soft image is superimposed over a sharp image. With the stronger diffusion filters, the soft image is emphasized over the sharp image.

- With fog filters, the entire image is softened. The filter is like a fine-ground glass; the stronger the effect, the coarser the grind.

- A number of homemade devices can be used to soften, or diffuse, the image. Thin transparent sheeting, like the outer wrapping on a pack of cigarettes, can be crumpled lightly and straightened out. When used in front of the normal copy lens, the crumple lines provide the image diffusion. The straightened material can be stretched on a filter ring and trimmed, making a semi-permanent diffusion filter.

- Black tulle is an open, hexagonal weave material used for veils. Bridal veils are often white tulle. This can be dyed black or blackened with a felt-tip marking pen. Two layers stretched over a filter frame or embroidery hoop can make a semi-permanent diffusion filter. Nylon hosiery material used in the same way gives a greater degree of diffusion.

- Diffusion can be thought of as spreading light areas of the image over the dark areas. The effect is different when starting with a positive image than with a negative image. Generally the effect is most pleasing when making the original copy negative. Diffusion can be done when enlarging the copy negative by holding the diffusing filter just under the enlarging lens during the print exposure. However, since the shadows are light in the negative, this results in spreading the shadows over the highlights, often causing a dull-looking print.

- Because image light is spread by diffusion, the contrast of the image is usually lowered. The contrast can be adjusted in the usual ways, by increasing the negative developing time, by increasing the exposure on KODAK Professional Copy Film, or simply by printing on a higher-contrast grade paper.

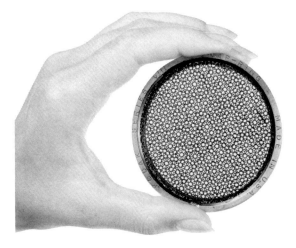

This diffuser is made with two layers of black tulle. It can be used over the camera lens while copying or over the enlarger lens when making the copy print. It should be kept moving during the exposure.

Printing Black-and-White Copy Negatives

The same principles and techniques that apply to printing camera original negatives are used to print copy negatives. There are some aspects worth mentioning here that make printing a copy negative different from printing an original negative. The first aspect is that only in certain situations will a copy print be better in quality than the original. An improvement in quality is possible most often with poor originals where the use of a special technique eliminates a gross defect. For example, a stained print will show a dramatic improvement when filtering is used to eliminate the stain. A torn print will look dramatically better if the tear can be cropped in copying or if it is retouched in a restoration technique. A low-contrast original will show a great improvement if the contrast is increased in copying. With a high-quality original, under ideal conditions, the best that a copy photographer can aim for is a black-and-white print that nearly equals the original in quality. When printing a copy negative the result is somewhat limited by the quality of the original. The importance of careful technique in copying cannot be overemphasized.

A second aspect in printing copy negatives is the importance of printing highlights to the proper density. With a poor-quality copy negative, lab technicians often make the mistake of printing the highlights darker than normal, in order to increase highlight tonal separation. The resultant print often looks muddy with little improvement in highlight detail. It is easily identified as a copy. With this type of copy negative, it usually improves the overall appearance of the print if the highlights are printed quite light in tone and the loss in highlight detail is accepted. A good copy negative with increased highlight contrast can be printed with normal highlight density and retain much of the detail that was in the original. (As previously mentioned, KODAK Professional Copy Film 4125 is designed to minimize the problem of muddy or low-contrast highlights by utilizing a characteristic curve shape that increases the contrast of highlight tones.) In either case, good judgment is necessary when determining highlight density, because highlights are often the most important tones in determining good print quality.

A third aspect is the contrast of the copy print. If the original is a high-quality original, it is desirable to match the contrast of the copy print to the original. Some burning-in or dodging may be necessary to match the density of the shadows and highlights to the original print or other local areas.

A final point is that most black-and-white papers increase slightly in density when they dry. This slight increase in density should be anticipated when judging wet prints for overall print quality. A copy print that matches the original when wet may appear too dark when it dries. This dry-down effect is generally most noticeable in the highlights.

COLOR COPYING TECHNIQUES

The procedures for copying with color films are similar to those of copying with black-and-white films. Of course, processing is different. Another difference is that in color copying, contrast cannot be controlled by adjusting developing times.

The major difference, however, in color copying is the necessity to maintain color balance throughout the copying procedure.

It is necessary to match the color balance of the lights and film when copying in color either by the choice of lights and film or by the use of filters.

Color Balance, Films, and Lights

When tungsten bulbs are used as the light source, it is best to use tungsten-balanced films. For occasional copying, a conversion filter can be used to balance tungsten lights to daylight film. The following KODAK WRATTEN Gelatin Filters can be used to balance lights of various color temperatures for use with daylight-balanced films.

3000 K (Enlarger bulbs) 80A + 82A
3200 K (Studio lamps) 80A
3400 K (Reflector-floods) 80B

An exact balance is desirable when copying on color transparency and slide films. Color negative camera films can be exposed with the wrong lamps and correction made when making prints. However, this makes color printing more difficult and can lower the color print quality as the result of different exposure levels in the three-color emulsion layers of the film which gives different density ranges in the different layers. KODAK VERICOLOR Internegative Films must be exposed to the correct balance illumination.

Although KODAK VERICOLOR II Professional Film 4108, Type L and the several KODAK VERICOLOR Internegative Films are basically tungsten-balanced, they usually require exact balancing with CC filters. The other KODAK VERICOLOR Films designed for camera use are daylight-balanced. KODAK EKTACHROME Papers used for direct-print copying are tungsten-balanced but also usually require fine-tuning with filters.

When color copies are being made for halftone reproduction, transparency films are usually chosen. Slide films are normally used for copies being made for projection. The Kodak films for tungsten use are
EKTACHROME 64T Professional Film,
EKTACHROME 160T Professional Film,
EKTACHROME 160T Film,
EKTACHROME 320T Professional Film, and
KODACHROME 40 Film 5070 (Type A).
Electronic flash is the daylight-balanced source commonly used . Pulsed xenon is not recommended for use with color films. All of the daylight-balanced films, both negative and transparency, can be used with electronic flash with minimal color balance filtration. Some arc lamps are suitable for color copying with daylight films. They provide high levels of illumination but require special installation and considerable filtration, which varies with the type of arc.

When an overall balance is achieved by proper choice of lamps and film, minor variations in balance are not generally required for color negative camera films. However, with transparency and slide films and with KODAK VERICOLOR Internegative Films, it is usually necessary to control color reproduction to a fairly close balance using light-balancing filters and/or color compensating filters.

Handling the Original

Color prints, printed illustrations, artwork, and fabrics are all commonly copied in color. Originals that are unmounted or large present the most difficult handling problems.

Color prints can be damaged very easily, particularly if they are unmounted. Unmounted prints are susceptible to crimp marks and bends from handling. Once a crimp or a bend has been made in a color print, it cannot be removed, and it will almost certainly show up in the copy. Fingerprints are also a hazard. Color prints can be marred by fingerprints very easily. Because of this, it is prudent to wear white cotton gloves when handling color prints. Color prints can be dusted clean with a camel's hair brush or a soft cloth.

Unmounted printed originals are also susceptible to crimps and bends, particularly large sheets of thin, coated paper. Unmounted originals can be positioned for shooting in a vertical copy setup by simply laying the original flat on the copyboard. If the original has a tendency to curl, low-profile weights or tacks can be used to hold it flat. Vacuum easels or copyboards are useful for holding thin originals flat.

A clean sheet of glass can also be used to hold an unmounted original flat.

In a horizontal copy setup, unmounted originals must be pinned or tacked. A magnetic copyboard may also be used.

Artwork such as paintings, drawings, or advertising comprehensives deserve special care. The value of such an original makes careful handling important. Do not attempt to clean or erase a mark on artwork.

Tapestries or textiles usually must be stretched taut before they can be photographed. In most instances, glass cannot be used to hold fabrics flat if the fabric has much texture. The glass tends to crush or flatten the fibers that impart the three-dimensional quality to the fabric.

A good way to mount a fabric for copying is to pin it in several places so that it does not show evidence of stretching.

Large unmounted color originals can be handled in the same way that a blueprint or a map would be handled. The original can be pinned or tacked to a large board when copying horizontally or laid flat for vertical copying.

Choosing a KODAK Color Film for Copying

As indicated earlier in connection with black-and-white copying, the first criterion of a film is that it fit the camera. Not all color films are available in all formats.

Camera Formats and KODAK Color Films: Most custom color copying is done with view cameras that use sheet films. The 4 x 5-inch size is the most commonly used. When process cameras are used, 8 x 10-inch and larger film sizes may be used (11 x 14-inch, 30 x 40 cm). Nearly all the color films that are used for copying are available in sheet film formats.

Sheet film cameras are the only ones suitable for direct copying on color reversal papers such as KODAK EKTACHROME Papers.

Most copying films are also available in the long roll format used in high-production copy cameras. The 35mm, 46mm, and 70mm widths, both perforated and unperforated, are made in many color emulsions. Larger-width rolls are also available.

Color negative VERICOLOR Films are available in 35mm magazines. KODAK Commercial Internegative Film is available in 35mm perforated long rolls. All the color slide films in both EKTACHROME and KODACHROME Film emulsions are available in 135 size magazines.

Not many color copy films are available for cameras that use 120 or 220 size film. For current availability of color films for copying, contact your photo dealer.

CHOOSING FILMS FOR COLOR PRINTS

Color negative films are recommended if the end product is a color print. The tone reproduction is more accurate than copying on a color transparency film and printing on a color reversal paper. Kodak internegative films are designed specifically to copy transparencies or color prints. As with black-and-white KODAK Professional Copy Film discussed earlier, these films are designed to give added contrast in the highlights to compensate for the compression of highlight tones that occurs when the negative is printed.

For this reason, more accurate copy tone reproduction can be achieved with internegative films when they are properly used. KODAK VERICOLOR Internegative Film 4112 in sheets is the film recommended for copying prints (and transparencies). KODAK Commercial Internegative Film 4325 and 5325 is recommended for copying transparencies only. These films are the only color films made by Kodak for the specific purpose of color copying and in general, are among the best films available for this purpose.

The successful use of Kodak internegative films requires critical exposure balance control achieved primarily through the use of color densitometry. Without this type of control, mismatched contrast in the three dye layers is highly probable, resulting in negatives that are impossible to print without tinted highlights or shadows. If no such control is available, it is more practical to aim for the next-best quality level by the use of VERICOLOR Films for cameras.

The following listings give the Kodak color films generally used for copying, with some information about the particular copying uses and characteristics.

COLOR NEGATIVE FILMS
- KODAK VERICOLOR Internegative Film 4112

This film gives fine tone reproduction in copies of prints, other full-tone reflection copy, and transparencies. It is used where the final result is to be a copy print. Its use will provide great reproduction of highlights and pastel colors from full-tone originals. All the color internegative films are balanced to be used with tungsten (3200 K) lamps. Some color compensating filter balancing is usually required.

KODAK VERICOLOR Internegative Film is capable of producing great color copy negatives, but

its use requires great care. The exposure must be precise to maintain the proper tone reproduction, and the color balance must be precise to keep the same contrast in the three dye images. This means that more measurement and testing needs to be done to obtain consistent working conditions for optimum results. Use of exposure meters for determining exposure and a color densitometer to control the negative density ranges in each dye layer are almost mandatory. Details of these controls are given starting on page 69.

- KODAK Commercial Internegative Film 4325 and 5325

This film is recommended when copying KODACHROME and EKTACHROME Film color transparencies. The density-difference method of exposure balancing control is suggested. Details of this method are given in a later section.

This internegative film has the same basic curve shape as the other internegative films. It has an upsweep in the curve to give expanded highlight-region tone reproduction to correct for the tone compression in the papers on which prints are made.

When this film is balanced, exposed, and processed accurately, it produces very high-quality results.

KODAK Color Negative Camera Films: As with black-and-white copying, color negative camera films intended for photographic use outside the laboratory can also be used for color copying. In general, these camera films have straight-line characteristic curves and tend to give compressed shadow and highlight tones, and expanded middle tones in the copy prints. This gives good color reproduction in the middle tones but tends to wash out the light tones and block-up the dark tones. If a color densitometer is not available to control the use of VERICOLOR Internegative Film, it may be better to use a color negative camera film even though the potential tone-reproduction quality may not be as high. The advantages offered by the use of KODAK VERICOLOR Internegative Film are highly dependent on correct usage with densitometric control. Used without this control, results are very likely to be poorer than if color negative camera film was used.

KODAK TRANSPARENCY AND SLIDE FILMS

As mentioned earlier, copy transparencies are useful when the copy is to be used to make halftone reproductions or when the transparencies (slides) are to be projected. When transparencies are used to make reflection copy prints, quality losses occur that are greater than those that occur when color negative films are used. Copy slides are generally made when the copies are to be used for projection. A flashing technique can be used to lower the contrast, if necessary. See page 79.

KODAK EKTACHROME Duplicating Film 6121 (Process E-6) and KODAK EKTACHROME Slide Duplicating Film 5071 are the laboratory films of choice for making transparency duplicates. Their use is discussed later in detail. Some camera films are occasionally used to "copy" transparencies.

KODAK EKTACHROME Films are available in many formats: sheets, rolls, long rolls, and 35mm magazines. KODACHROME Films other than KODACHROME 64 Professional Film are only available in 35mm magazines; KODACHROME 64 Professional Film is also available in 120 rolls.

Tungsten Films: KODAK EKTACHROME 64T Professional Film in rolls and sheets is designed to be used with exposure times near 5 seconds, although it can be used over a range of 1/10 second to 100 seconds and, of course, with tungsten illumination (3200 K). The effective speed of this film changes with the exposure time, and specific speeds are given on the instruction sheet packaged with the film for exposure times of 1/2, 5, 30, and 100 seconds. The speeds given include the exposure increase required by the CC filter(s) recommended to compensate for reciprocity effects.

KODAK EKTACHROME 160T Professional Film in rolls is a similar film but is color balanced for an exposure time of 1/10 second. Its recommended range of exposure times is from 1/100 second to 10 seconds. The effective speed of each roll is printed on the instruction sheet.

KODACHROME 40 Film 5070 (Type A) is balanced for photolamps (3400 K). It is designed for exposure times from 1/10,000 second to 10 seconds. Exposure times longer than 1/10 second require a correction for reciprocity. KODACHROME Films are especially recommended when long-term dark-storage stability is desired, although current EKTACHROME Films also have excellent dark-storage stability.

Daylight Films: KODAK EKTACHROME 64 Professional Film 6117 (Daylight) in sheets is a good choice when the copy transparencies are to be used for halftone reproduction and when electronic flash is the illumination. It can be used for exposure times from 1/10,000 second to 10 seconds. Reciprocity exposure time correction and CC filter correction is necessary at the shortest time and for times 1 second and longer. KODAK EKTACHROME 64 Professional Film 6017 (Daylight) is available in 120 and 220 size rolls, long rolls (5017), and 35mm magazines (5017).

KODACHROME 25 Film (Daylight) is available only in 35mm, while KODACHROME 64 Professional Film comes in both 35mm and 120 rolls. KODACHROME 25 Film can be used for exposure times from 1/10,000 second to 100 seconds, while KODACHROME 64 Film can be used for exposure times from 1/10,000 second to 1 second. Corrections for reciprocity are required with the longer exposure times. The contrast of copies made on KODACHROME Films is high and is generally reduced by flashing.

Using Faster Color Films For Copying: As indicated earlier, it is usually an advantage to use the slower-speed films for copying because finer grain and increased sharpness are usually achieved. However, there are times when a faster film offers considerable advantage with either color negative or transparency film. One situation is where lighting levels are such that extremely long exposure times are necessary, such as in dimly-lit museums where the use of a tripod and/or auxiliary lights is forbidden. Another is when correction or polarizing filters are used that reduce the effective film speed considerably. This is especially true when polarizing screens are placed over the lights and a polarizing filter is placed over the camera lens. Under these circumstances, the finer grain and increased sharpness of the slower film can be exchanged for a faster film speed. The following films can be used in these circumstances, but the user must be willing to accept the attendant lowering of quality.

Faster KODAK Color Negative Films

VERICOLOR III Professional Film, Type S	ISO 160 Daylight
Pro 400 Film	ISO 400 Daylight
Pro 400 MC Film	ISO 400 Daylight
GOLD 400 Film	ISO 400 Daylight
ROYAL GOLD 400 Film	ISO 400 Daylight
ROYAL GOLD 1000 Film	ISO 1000 Daylight

Faster KODAK Color Transparency Films

EKTACHROME 200
    Professional Film   ISO 200 Daylight
EKTACHROME 400X
    Professional Film   ISO 400 Daylight
EKTACHROME 160T
    Professional Film   ISO 160 Tungsten
EKTACHROME 320T
    Professional Film   ISO 320 Tungsten

The films mentioned in this section are Kodak color films suitable for copying that are available as this book is written. Eastman Kodak Company reserves the right to change and improve products at any time. It is therefore likely that some of the films mentioned above may have been replaced by the time you read this. The replacement films may work for copying and duplicating purposes just as well as the current films. It is wise to make a choice of films based on the principles presented in this book and to run tests to see that the new choice produces satisfactory results. Be sure to match the color balance of the film to the color temperature of the light source, to base the exposure on the listed film speed, and to choose properly between fast and slow films and between color negative and transparency films.

Lighting and Exposure

The basic concepts of lighting and exposure are the same as in black-and-white copying. The biggest difference when copying in color is that the spectral sensitivity of the film (color balance) should be selected to match the color temperature of the light source.

Kodak color films are usually balanced for exposure to 5500 K light sources or 3200 K light sources. Film balanced for exposure to 5500 K illumination is referred to as daylight-balanced film. Film balanced for 3200 K illumination is referred to as tungsten-balanced film. One film that does not fall into these two categories is KODACHROME 40 Film 5070 (Type A). This film is color-balanced for 3400 K illumination. KODAK VERICOLOR Internegative Film is balanced for 3200 K illumination but nearly always requires the use of CC filters to balance the dye layer contrast.

Color balancing filters can be used to match unlike films and light sources. A list on page 18 shows what filters are necessary with several film and light-source combinations.

Some light sources that work well with black-and-white materials are unsuitable for critical color photography. Fluorescent light sources and pulsed-xenon sources, for example, should be avoided because of the difficulty in obtaining good color balance.

In general, color negative camera films with straight-line characteristic curves have much more latitude with film/light-source color match than VERICOLOR Internegative Film. The latter, however, gives improved highlight tone reproduction. A great deal of color control can be exercised in the printing step. Color transparency films require much closer attention to color balance.

When color transparency films are used in copying, it is a very good idea to expose and process a test transparency first before shooting many originals. Even when the light source and the film type have been matched as recommended, critical color balance usually requires that color correction filters be used. Color balance corrections can be determined with the *KODAK Color Print Viewing Filter Kit,* Publication R-25. This is a kit containing magenta, red, yellow, green, cyan, and blue filters. The correct color balance of a transparency or print can be determined by viewing it through the filter that neutralizes the color cast.

Several light-source variables can affect the color balance of the reproduction. The age of the light bulbs (especially tungsten light sources other than quartz iodine or tungsten halogen) can have an effect on the color balance. The color balance of the lights may shift through the life of the bulbs. Electronic flash units emit varying amounts of ultraviolet radiation which may photograph bluish on color film. Diffusers and reflectors can also impart a color cast to a copy. The flash from automatic units can also change color balance when taking extreme close-ups because the flash duration is shortened considerably.

Minor speed corrections for KODAK EKTACHROME Professional Films are printed on the instruction sheets packaged with the film. This is information about the particular emulsion and is based on manufacturing tests.

REFLECTIONS AND COLOR CONTAMINATION

For color copying, control over copyboard illumination is even more critical than with black-and-white copying. Room lights should be turned off even if they are dim. Room lights are seldom the correct color temperature and can cause a color cast or reflections in the copy either by direct illumination or by illuminating a wall that may reflect the wrong color light on the original. This color cast is called color contamination, because it is caused by a source of illumination other than the copy lights.

Other sources of color contamination are windows (daylight), colored walls, colored ceilings, and colored furniture. These objects should not be located next to a copy setup.

Ideally, a color-copying room should have black walls and a black ceiling with no windows. If a window is located near a copy setup, opaque black shades can be used to minimize the daylight illumination.

Processing Color Films

KODAK VERICOLOR Films (including the internegative films) are processed in the Process C-41 with KODAK FLEXICOLOR Chemicals. KODAK EKTACHROME Films are processed in the Process E-6 using KODAK EKTACHROME Chemicals. It is not practical for most users to process KODACHROME Films because of the complicated process.

The Processes C-41 and E-6 are of such a nature that they can, with care, be performed by any fairly proficient person. Many photofinishing and commercial laboratories provide processing services for those who do not wish to process their own films. Processing instructions for using the Processes C-41 and E-6 are given in *KODAK Color Darkroom DATAGUIDE,* Publication R-19.

In addition, concise instructions are packaged with E-6 and C-41 chemical kits and with the developers in the larger sizes of chemicals.

For large-volume processing with replenishment, control strip quality-control procedures are required.

For those already processing color films, there are no basic differences between processing copy negatives and regular camera negatives.

Special Techniques

COPYING REFLECTION COPY WITH KODAK VERICOLOR INTERNEGATIVE FILM 4112

KODAK VERICOLOR Internegative Film has the highest potential for producing quality copy negatives from which color copy prints are made, but the characteristics that give it this potential make it somewhat difficult to use. However, with adequate time spent learning the procedures for controlling exposure and color balance, any careful person should be able to make high-quality copy negatives with this film.

In order to build in the desired characteristics, six emulsion layers, plus nine separation, protective, and filter layers are required, making it among the most complex color films manufactured by Eastman Kodak Company. See illustration on page 111.

Because of the unique curve shapes, each layer must receive just the correct exposure by the user, both to put the exposure at the right place for the inflection point in the film curve shape to provide the best tone reproduction, and to balance all dye layers so that they print correctly.

Use of this film for optimum results for copying both reflection originals and transparencies requires precise exposure and light balancing, constant monitoring of results, and a level of technical competence to measure and control the results.

Tungsten illumination (3200 K studio lamps) is recommended for copying reflection flat-art originals on this film. Also recommended is the use of a KODAK WRATTEN Filter No. 2B over the camera lens to absorb the ultraviolet radiation.

It is important that the three basic layers receive the same relative exposures. To do this, KODAK Color Compensating Filters must usually be used over the camera lens. The correction varies with different emulsion numbers of internegative film—a starting pack is recommended for each package on the instruction sheet. If this is not available, use a starting pack of 30M + 30Y.

For the sheet film, the lights should be placed so that the copyboard receives about 100 footcandles of illumination. If an 18% KODAK Gray Card is placed on the copyboard and the lights adjusted until a reflected-light meter reading based on a film speed of ISO 125 indicates an exposure of 1/8 second at *f*/8, the 100-footcandle aim is achieved. This setting is used only to get the light level correct and is not an exposure reading. An exposure time of 10 seconds is nominal for this film.

This reproduction was made directly from a color print from an original color negative. This subject was chosen to show how well prints with a variety of colors can be copied.

This reproduction was made from a copy color print. The print above was copied on KODAK VERICOLOR Internegative Film 4112. Control of the internegative was provided by the curve-plotting method. The color match between the copy print and the original is generally good, but some colors do not match exactly.

The starting exposure on the sheet film emulsion should be about 10 seconds at f/5.6. The optimum range of exposure times is 7 seconds to 15 seconds.

A KODAK Gray Scale, such as that supplied in the *KODAK Color Separation Guide and Gray Scale* (KODAK Publication No. Q-13 or Q-14), should be included with the copy. The image on the film should be large enough so that the images of the gray scale steps can be measured with a densitometer.

The following basic exposure series should be made:
    At f/8 4112 film:
    5, 7, 10, 14, and 20 seconds
    (100 fc illum)

The test films are processed normally in Process C-41 using KODAK FLEXICOLOR Chemicals. The negatives are then checked to see that the cyan, magenta, and yellow dye images are very close in contrast.

Kodak suggests two methods of checking copy color negatives made from reflection copy with KODAK VERICOLOR Internegative Film. The first is a visual method, the second is a measurement-plotting method called the reference curve method.

VISUAL CHECK OF COLOR INTERNEGATIVES

The visual check method must be used if you do not have a color densitometer. It may take many trials to achieve a balanced negative using this method alone. The other use of the visual check method is to verify the results of the reference curve method.

This method requires making test color prints. The first test is made on KODAK EKTACOLOR Paper and is balanced for the middle gray tones on the reproduction of the gray scale. It may take several filter adjustments and trial prints to achieve the balanced neutrals.

If the highlight and shadow tones are neutral when the midtones are neutral, the negative has satisfactory color balance, that is, the three dye images have the same contrast and the curves are said to be parallel and not crossed.

If, however, the highlights have a cast of one color while the shadows have a cast of the complementary color, the negative is out of balance and is said to have crossed curves. The strength of the color cast gives a clue to how far it is out of balance.

The filter pack on the copy camera is changed to correct the balance. The correction is made by subtracting filtration of the color cast in the highlights. If the highlights are yellowish, for example, yellow filtration is subtracted from the pack. If there is no yellow in the pack, filtration of the complementary color is added to the packs. In our example, blue filtration is added.

The table on page 73 summarizes this procedure, gives guidance on how great a filter change to make, and indicates how to change the camera exposure in order to compensate for the change in filtration.

A new internegative is then made. Another test print is made, again balanced for the middle gray tones on the gray scale. This new print is evaluated.

If the print highlights have the same color as the first print, but less of it, the filter change was in the right direction but was not great enough. In our example, more yellow should be subtracted from the packs. If the highlights are now blue, too much yellow was subtracted, and some yellow filtration is added back in the camera pack. Of course, when the highlights and shadows are neutral, the correction was just right.

This procedure is repeated until an acceptably neutral gray scale is achieved.

When a balance is obtained for a given emulsion of the film, many copies can be made as long as all the factors stay the same—emulsion number, lights, camera filter pack, process, etc. When one of the factors changes, a new test may be required to find the proper balance for the changed conditions.

CURVE-PLOTTING METHOD OF BALANCING

To balance internegative film by plotting curves, a series of copy negatives of the *KODAK Gray Scale* (Publication No. Q-13 or Q-14) is made on KODAK VERICOLOR Internegative Film as described earlier.

After processing, the A steps on the gray scale of the negatives are measured with the red filter (status M) on the densitometer. The negative is chosen that has a density value in this step of between 1.30 to 1.50, preferably about 1.40.

The red, green, and blue densities of each of the steps in this negative are measured on a color densitometer with status M filters. Each density is plotted on *KODAK Curve-Plotting Graph Paper*, Publication E-64.

Row C on the curve-plotting paper lists the steps of the Q-13 or Q-14 gray scale.

A smooth curve is then drawn through a line of best fit for the plotted points creating characteristic curves of the cyan, magenta, and yellow layers. The curve for the cyan dye layer is usually called the red curve, because it is measured with the red filter on the densitometer and is a record of the red content of the original. Likewise the magenta dye-layer curve is called the green curve, and the yellow dye-layer curve is called the blue curve.

The plotted curves represent the inherent charac-

72

Guide for Adjusting Filter Pack When Making Internegatives

If Highlights in Print Are	If Shadows in Print Are	Either		Or	
		Subtract These Filters from Pack	And Multiply Exposure by	Add These Filters to Pack	And Multiply Exposure by
Cyan	Red	20C	0.91	20R	1.5
Magenta	Green	20M	0.91	20G	1.3
Yellow	Blue	20Y	0.91	20B	1.6
Red	Cyan	20R	0.67	20C	1.1
Green	Magenta	20G	0.77	20M	1.1
Blue	Yellow	20B	0.59	20Y	1.1
Cyan	Red	10C	0.91	10R	1.3
Magenta	Green	10M	0.91	10G	1.2
Yellow	Blue	10Y	0.91	10B	1.3
Red	Cyan	10R	0.77	10C	1.1
Green	Magenta	10G	0.83	10M	1.1
Blue	Yellow	10B	0.77	10Y	1.1

Note: It is generally more desirable to modify a filter pack by subtracting filters rather than by adding them.

teristics of the particular emulsion combined with the modifying effects of the photographic system including camera flare, film process, etc. In an earlier section on copy camera setup, attention was called to the various factors that reduce the flare level. These are especially important in copying on VERICOLOR Internegative Film.

- Clean camera lens.
- Clean and relatively scratch-free filters.
- Black copyboard surround for the original copy material.
- Effective lens hood.
- Clean and matte-black camera interior.
- Matte-black walls, ceiling, floor, window shades, etc., in the copy area.

When the three curves are plotted on the KODAK Curve-Plotting Graph Paper, the paper is placed over the KODAK Internegative Film (reflection) reference curves shown in the illustration on page 74. The reference lines of the graph are aligned over the reference lines in the illustration on the next page. Where the upper part of test curves fall in relation to the reference curves indicates how well the test negative has been balanced and exposed.

If all three test curves are higher than the reference curves, the negative is overexposed. A new test negative is made with less exposure. If all three test curves are lower than the reference curves, the negative is underexposed, and a new test negative is made with more exposure. The red curve is the key to the basic exposure. If the red curve is too high, reduce the overall exposure. If the red curve is too low, increase the overall exposure. When the red curve aligns with the reference curves, look at the other two curves for alignment. Misalignment of either curve means that the negative is out of balance. Correcting the balance is accomplished by using KODAK Color Compensating (CC) Filters over the camera lens.

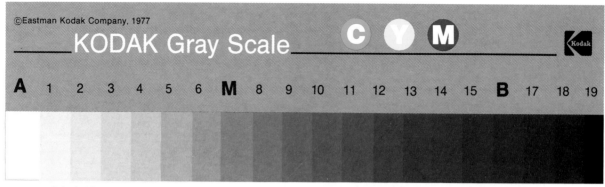

KODAK Gray Scale

A 1 2 3 4 5 6 M 8 9 10 11 12 13 14 15 B 17 18 19

Because of the halftone process in printing, some of the gradation between the steps of the KODAK Gray Scale is lost.

The curves change shape as the exposure is changed. In the illustration, note that the overexposed curve has a longer section of upsweep at the high density end. The underexposed curve has a shorter section of upsweep. Balancing the three curves using CC filters makes all three curves have the same amount of upsweep.

If the blue curve is high, that layer received too much exposure. Blue light is absorbed by yellow filters. Therefore, yellow filtration must be added to the pack (or blue filtration subtracted) to move the curve down.

If the blue curve is low, it received too little exposure, and the exposure is increased by removing yellow filtration.

If the green curve is high, add magenta filtration; if the green curve is low, take out magenta filtration.

The filter pack will generally contain yellow and magenta filtration to produce balanced copy negatives, so the changes will almost always be in these two colors. Green and blue are included in the table for the unusual circumstances when these colors are in the pack.

The following table summarizes the changes.

When the changes needed have been calculated, a new exposure is made incorporating these changes. The densities of the step images are measured and a new set of curves plotted. These curves should fall closer to the reference curves. Additional corrections and yet a third negative may be needed before all these curves come close to the reference curves.

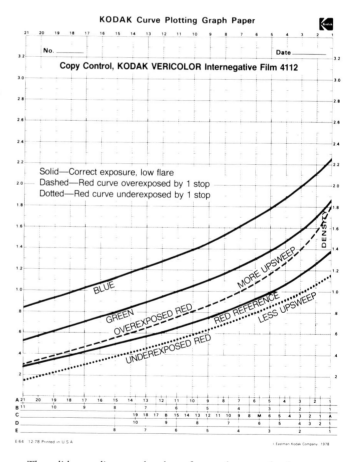

The solid curve lines are the plots of correctly exposed red, green, and blue curves. The dashed line represents the plot of an overexposed red curve, while the dotted line represents the plot of an underexposed red curve.

Curve Color	Curve Location	Correction Add Filtration	or Subtract Filtration
Red*	Too High	Cyan	Red
	Too Low	Red	Cyan
Green	Too High	Magenta	Green
	Too Low	Green	Magenta
Blue	Too High	Yellow	Blue
	Too Low	Blue	Yellow

*This correction is rarely used. Changing the camera exposure raises and lowers the red curve.

KODAK Curve Plotting Graph Paper

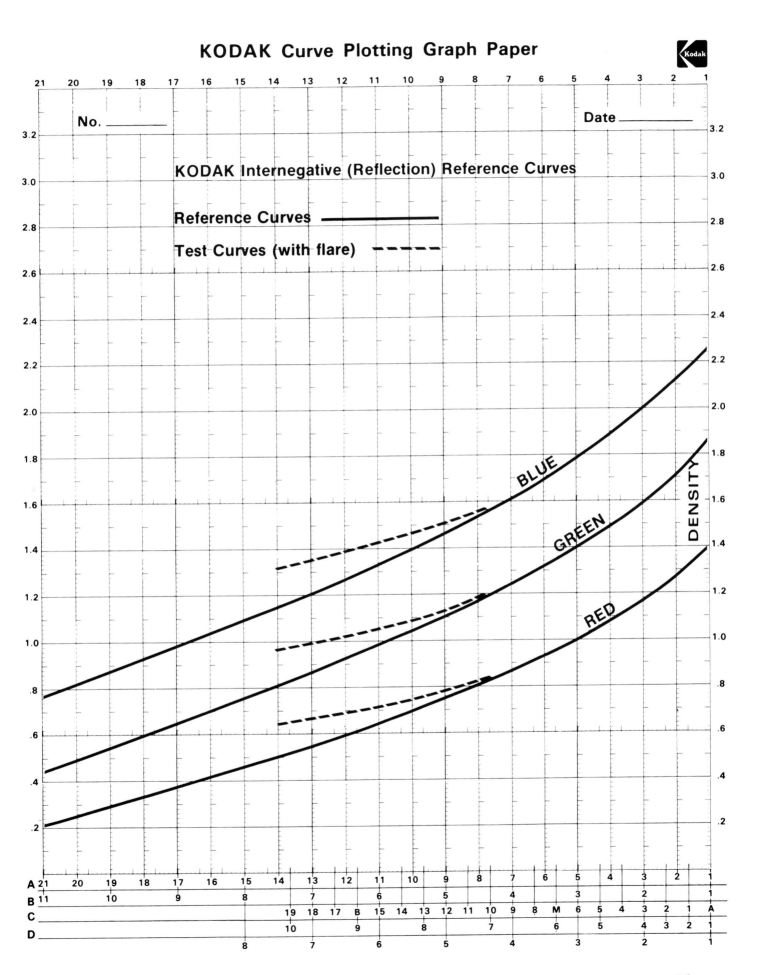

KODAK Internegative (Reflection) Reference Curves

Reference Curves ————————

Test Curves (with flare) — — — — —

No. _____   Date _____

75

COPYING FADED COLOR PRINTS

The technique of copying color prints on KODAK VERICOLOR Internegative Film 4112 offers a method of restoring faded color prints. Overall exposure increase is used to restore the lowered print contrast caused by the fading.

Usually one of the dye colors fades more than the others, resulting in a print that is no longer in balance. Using color compensating filters, a filter pack adjustment is made to give the most faded color layer additional exposure to raise its contrast (density range) to be equal to the others.

Copying with Other KODAK Color Films

COLOR NEGATIVE CAMERA FILMS

The special curve shape of KODAK VERICOLOR Internegative Film offers the possibility of improved tone reproduction in the highlight tones of copy prints made from them. As we have seen, this curve shape requires that the exposure of the three color images be fairly exact and very closely matched or the density differences as finally seen by the print material of the three layers will not match, making it impossible to balance the prints made from them. Thus careful control is required when copying with the internegative films.

Regular color negative camera films do not have this special curve shape because they are designed to photograph original subjects whose tone reproduction has not been distorted by having already been through one photographic process. The characteristic curves of camera films have nearly straight-line characteristic curves above the toe level. Therefore, within a limited range, when one imaging layer receives relatively more exposure than another, as when the light and film may be slightly out of balance, the one layer will have more density overall than the other layers but will have essentially the same density difference. Special filtering will be required in making the print, but the special filtering will produce a print that does not shift appreciably in color from highlight to shadow tones.

Thus, color negative camera films are much easier to use than the internegative films and do not require the very careful densitometric control described earlier.

In addition to highlight compression, another difficulty with using color negative camera film for copying is that the contrast is too high for most originals. The midtone contrast is increased in the copy print, and the negative density range is too great, leading to burned-out highlights and loss of shadow detail in the print.

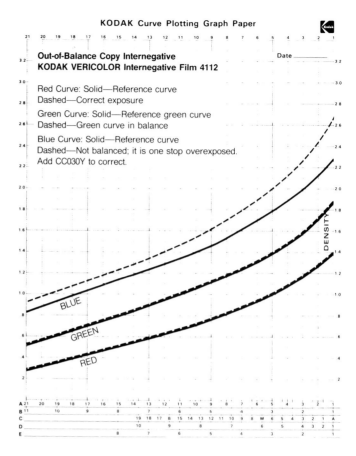

When the red curve on your test copy negative overlaps the standard red curve, the basic exposure is correct. In this plot, the green curve also overlaps the standard curve, indicating that the magenta balance is correct. However, the blue curve indicates overexposure of the blue layer, so the yellow balance is off. With the blue curve too high, yellow filtration should be added to the pack to lower the blue curve in the next test.

Comparisons of color prints made with KODAK VERICOLOR Internegative Film and a regular camera film, KODAK VERICOLOR II Professional Film 4108, Type L. This illustration was made from the original print.

This illustration was made from a copy print made from a copy negative on KODAK VERICOLOR Internegative Film 4112 (ESTAR Thick Base).

Using a color negative camera film as a copy film increases the contrast considerably. This illustration was made from a copy print from a copy negative on KODAK VERICOLOR II Professional Film 4108, Type L without flashing.

Giving a flash exposure to the regular color negative camera film reduces the contrast of the copy print. This illustration was made from a copy print on KODAK VERICOLOR II Professional Film 4108, Type L with a flash exposure of a white paper with 1.2 neutral density filtration. See text for details.

The solution to this problem is to give a flash exposure or fogging exposure to the film at the time the copy exposure is given. The following procedure seems to work satisfactorily with most Kodak color negative camera films.

1. Give normal copy exposure.
2. Place white paper on the copyboard. Fixed-out white photographic black-and-white paper works well.
3. Place 1.2 neutral density filters over the lens.
4. Give the film the same exposure (same exposure time, same f-number) for the flash exposure.
5. Process normally.

KODAK VERICOLOR III Professional Film, Type S has slightly lower contrast than the other Kodak color negative films so requires less flash exposure. A 1.3 to 1.4 neutral density filtration should work well with this film.

If the negative contrast is too low, increase the value of the neutral density filtration, or if the contrast is too high, decrease the amount of neutral density filtration.

In summary, the highest quality copies can be made with VERICOLOR Internegative Film with densitometric control. Quite satisfactory copies can be made with flashed color negative camera films without densitometric control.

The different color negative camera films have different reciprocity characteristics. In general, Type S films are designed for short exposure times while Type L films are designed for longer exposure times.

There is usually no need to use high-speed color negative films. However, when copying in a museum where no additional lights are allowed, the use of 1000-speed films should be considered.

The color negative camera films are processed normally and the negatives are printed normally. Some degree of contrast control can be achieved by the choice of paper. Printing on KODAK EKTACOLOR PORTRA II Paper will produce slightly lower-contrast prints.

COPYING ON TRANSPARENCY FILM

Copying reflection originals using transparency film is different than copying with negative film because there is only one opportunity to make exposure and color correction adjustments. The exposure and color correction must be correct the first time. Unlike color negative films, there is very little overexposure latitude. It is better to underexpose slightly rather than to overexpose. If the color balance is off slightly, it must be corrected by reshooting or by duplicating. Lighting unevenness cannot be corrected by burning-in or dodging, as it can be during the printing of a color negative.

As mentioned previously, because of the need for precise exposure and color correction, it is advisable to make a test before copying many originals. The test will confirm exposure and color balance. Color transparency film requires correct color balance more than most color negative camera films. KODAK Color Compensating Filters, used over the camera lens, can be used for fine-tuning color balance. The *KODAK Color Print Viewing Filter Kit*, Publication R-25, is helpful for determining the exact filtration. It is also helpful to include standard color checkers and a KODAK Gray Scale to monitor the reproduction of colors and tones.

Controlling Contrast of Transparency Films: The contrast of various KODAK EKTACHROME Films can be varied by changing the first development time or temperature (push or pull processing) of the Process E-6. A moderate change in color balance may occur when the process is changed. This can be corrected by the use of color compensating filters. The following table can be used as a starting point for experimentation.

Exposure-Development Changes for Control With Process E-6

Contrast Change	Exposure Index Change	First Development Time Change	or	Temperature Change
Maximum Increase	+ 3 stops	+ 10 minutes		+ 16 F
Moderate Increase	+ 2 stops	+ 5 minutes		+ 12 F
Slight Increase	+ 1 stop	+ 2 minutes		+ 8 F
Slight Decrease	− 1 stop	− 2 minutes		− 6 F
Moderate Decrease	− 2 stops	− 3 minutes		− 13 F
Considerable Decrease	− 3 stops	Not recommended		− 16 F
Maximum Decrease	− 4 stops	Not recommended		− 19 F

A first development adjustment to raise contrast results in lower D-max and warm color balance. Temperature adjustment to lower contrast is preferred to time adjustment because there is less highlight degradation. Compensation to lower contrast results in cold color balance, especially in the highlight region.

Flashing is a method of lowering contrast that can be used with both EKTACHROME and KODACHROME Films*. A brief exposure to a white card is commonly used. A neutral density filter with a density value of from 1.6 to 2.0 is put over the lens, the white card is placed in front of the original copy, and an exposure of the same shutter speed and *f*-number as the main exposure is given. This lowers the D-max and the contrast. Using a 2.0 neutral density filter gives a minimum effect, using a 1.6 density filter lowers the contrast considerably. If the shadows appear "milky," the flash exposure is too great and is lessened by using a higher value ND filter. When the contrast is changed by flashing, normal processing is used.

Where lower contrast transparencies are desired, KODAK EKTACHROME Duplicating Film or KODAK EKTACHROME Duplicating Slide Film can be used as a copy film. The contrast of these films is lower than camera transparency color films because they are made to duplicate (copy) color transparencies which are generally higher in contrast than original subjects. It is not necessary to flash this film to achieve low-contrast results.

Another control that is available to increase contrast moderately is polarizing filters. When polarizing filters are used both over the lens and the lights, as described in the section "Using Polarizing Filters," contrast increases noticeably. To a lesser extent, contrast also increases when using a polarizing filter over the lens only.

*This procedure is similar to that used with color negative films. A higher neutral density value is used with transparency films.

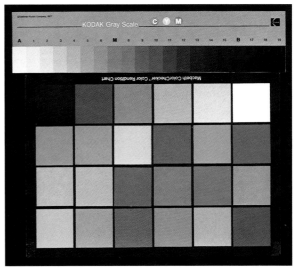

Flashing is useful to lower the copy contrast when copying with transparency films as well as with color negative films. The above illustration was made from a copy transparency without flashing.

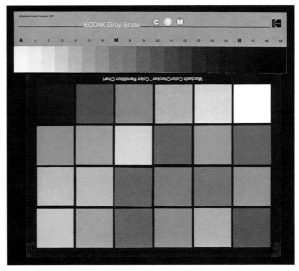

This illustration was made from a copy transparency on the same film but an additional flash exposure of white paper was given using 1.7 neutral density filtration.

Direct Copying with
KODAK EKTACHROME RADIANCE Paper

Photographers and art directors are often in a rush to obtain copies of color photographs, artwork, or layouts. Fast turnaround times can be achieved by copying directly onto KODAK EKTACHROME RADIANCE Paper. It is available in several sizes. The copy is made by exposing the reversal material in a view or process camera focused on the original.

With EKTACHROME RADIANCE Paper, laterally reversed images will occur unless a mirror is used in front of the camera lens to correct the image orientation. This can be accomplished by positioning a front-surface mirror at a 45° angle in front of the lens. EKTACHROME RADIANCE Paper can also be used in some copy machines that combine camera and processor into one unit. Available from other manufacturers, these units can be used in normal room light.

EKTACHROME RADIANCE Paper can be processed in a drum or a tray with KODAK EKTACHROME R-3000 Chemicals or in a machine processor with EKTACHROME R-3 Chemicals.

Standard copying equipment will fulfill most needs. Tungsten-balanced lights (3200 K) are preferred because these reversal materials are tungsten-balanced. Other items that might be used are a tripod, a copyboard, KODAK Color Compensating (CC) Filters, and a *KODAK Color Print Viewing Filter Kit,* Publication R-25.

The copy setup can be arranged like any other copy setup using the view camera. The color copy is secured to the copyboard, and the image is sized and focused on the ground glass. A sheet film holder is loaded with EKTACHROME RADIANCE Paper and exposed in the camera. A camera equipped with a vacuum film back (such as a large graphic arts copy camera) can hold all sizes of film or paper without a film holder.

Determine exposure with an exposure test. A convenient method of making a test exposure is to use a piece of black copyboard over the copy to step off a series of exposures on one sheet of film. Intervals of five or ten seconds can be used. A starting point for making a test, copying at 1:1, using two 250 W photolamps placed 3 feet from the copyboard (on both sides at 45°), would be 5, 10, 15, and 20 seconds at *f*/8.

From the processed test sheet, the best exposure can be determined by choosing the time required to produce the most pleasing density (with reversal film or paper, more exposure gives less density).

KODAK EKTACHROME RADIANCE Copy Paper works well when copying continuous-tone originals or, as in this example, originals that have both continuous tone and line copy.

Color balance can be evaluated by viewing the print with filters from the KODAK Color Print Viewing Filter Kit. The evaluation should be made by viewing the print under the same type of illumination that will be used to display the print. It is usually helpful to compare the color balance of the copy to the original. Select a filter from the kit that makes the midtones of the copy appear close in color to the original. The value of the selected filter is the value of the CC filter required over the camera lens. In general, if the print looks cool, warm-colored filters (magenta, red, or yellow) will correct the color. If the print appears warm, cool-colored filters (green, cyan, or blue) will correct the color.

Once color balance has been established for a given set of circumstances, the color balance for successive copies should be very close. Minor adjustment may be necessary with different packages of film or paper and as the copy lights age.

Original illustration.

Copy made on Kodak reversal film.

Copying Paintings and Other Art Originals

Copying paintings and artwork is one of the most difficult types of copying. Each original must be photographed with the sensitivity and skill that would be required of a portrait or a studio illustration. Each original presents different technical problems that must be overcome.

Art is photographed for many different purposes. The most common purpose is for halftone reproduction. A print or a transparency is much more convenient and useful to give to a printer than the original artwork. Whenever halftone illustrations are required for book illustrations, posters, or catalogs, a photographic print or transparency is made first. The color balance of the copy, the contrast, and the lighting are all extremely important.

Another purpose for photographing art is for documentation. For example, photographs are often needed for insurance records or for inventory files. Several views might be required showing scale, thickness, condition, or significant details. The intent is different than when photographing to make an illustration. Cosmetic appearance is not as important as detail and scale. For this type of photograph, a ruler or other object that has size recognition is helpful to include in the frame of the picture to identify the size of the original. Close-up views that help show such features as condition or authenticity may also be helpful.

Also, damage to artwork from an accident or vandalism is often photographed for file and insurance records.

Photographs may be required prior to the restoration of a painting. Cracks, scratches, dents, or other blemishes would be emphasized so that a before-and-after comparison can be made. The back side of a painting must be photographed when it is to be put on a new stretcher or if it will be relined with new canvas so that any important historical information is recorded.

Artwork must be handled with extreme care. When positioning artwork for copying, the method for securing the artwork must not in any way damage the original or interfere with the lighting. Several methods for securing paper artworks are illustrated here. The idea behind each method is to ensure that the securing system does not puncture or create a dent in the surface of the paper but still proves a safe method for holding the original flat. For this reason pins and tacks should never be used directly on a valuable original. Adhesives should not be used for securing artwork because certain adhesives may cause permanent damage. Also, it is important that tacks or pins, used as illustrated, are

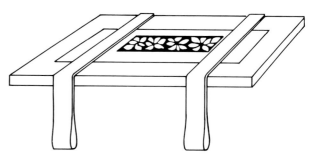

When many copies of flat art are being copied on a vertical copy stand, two weighted straps can be made as a quick and safe way to hold the art flat. The art must have borders.

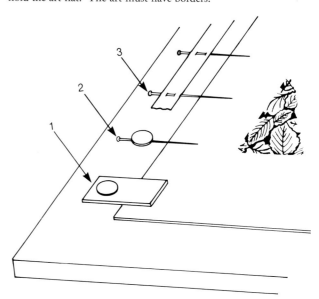

Three methods are shown for holding unmounted art without putting pinholes in it. (1) a tab of stiff cardboard is held with beeswax, (2) a pin is pushed through a small dab of beeswax, and (3) pins are pushed through masking tape which is then stuck to the copy stand.

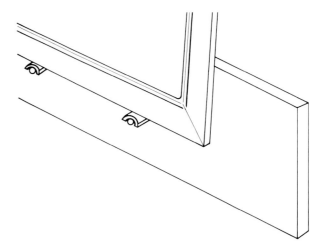

Framed art can be held against a wall for horizontal copying. Small pads placed on the nails protect the frame. These can be made of masking tape rolled into small cylinders with the sticky side inside.

positioned so that they do not cast shadows on the copy. Push pins or other high-profile tacks may be unsatisfactory because of the shadows they cast.

A heavy framed painting can be supported on a sturdy easel for photographing or it can be supported on two large nails in a wall. A small piece of padding between the frame and the nails is necessary to prevent damage to the frame.

No attempt should be made to clean a painting or other art original. If the appearance of a painting needs to be improved for reproduction, the job should be left to an expert. An inexperienced person cleaning a painting could cause considerable damage that might result in a lawsuit being brought against the photographer.

When storing artwork that is to be photographed, keep it away from extremes of heat, humidity, and light. It is a good practice to cover or enclose artwork when it is not being photographed to provide protection from dust and dirt.

Techniques: Once the painting or other type of artwork is mounted securely the next task is to light it. The basic setup is the same as for a routine copy. Two lights on each side of the original at 45° to the copyboard will suffice for many types of flat art. Many of the precautions for avoiding flare and unwanted reflections that would be taken in any good copy setup should also be observed here. Room lights should be made as dim as possible, and the surrounding walls should either be painted a dark neutral color or should be far enough away from the copy so that reflections and color contamination are not a problem. Gobos (a shading device on a gooseneck), lens shades, and barn doors (black metal flaps on the front of spotlights to control light spread) are all useful to help control unwanted stray light.

The format of the copy film is generally determined by the end use of the copy. For high-quality color reproductions (posters, book illustrations) a large-format film is preferred. A color transparency is usually more acceptable than a print for photomechanical reproduction. 35mm slides are commonly used for less critical purposes and for audiovisual shows.

Oil or acrylic paintings that have a glossy surface must be handled with special care to avoid reflections or color contamination.

The ideal environment for photographing paintings is in a black room with a dark floor. The illustration on page 84 shows how one photographer who specializes in photographing artwork has solved these problems. In his studio portable matte-black flats are used to block off stray light to the sides of the painting. They are also used to shade the camera from stray light that may come from the back of the lights. Most studio photographers have painted flats, or

free-standing panels made out of PVC tubing or other materials that are equipped to take sheets of white or black fabric, to either reflect light or to absorb and block it.

A black background is provided behind the paintings to reduce flare in the camera. A dark neutral-colored cloth is used to cover the floor in front of the painting to avoid a reflection from the floor. In this studio the ceiling is also painted black to prevent reflections. These precautions are not necessary for every painting that is copied, but they are necessary when a large shiny-surfaced painting is to be photographed and represent the optimum arrangement.

When paintings are copied for reproduction they are most often copied in color. In order to judge the quality of the copy and to monitor the reproduction process, it is helpful to include a gray scale and a color scale. KODAK Publications Q-13 (small) and Q-14 (large) include both of these scales. A gray scale is helpful for judging exposure and contrast. The color scale is useful for determining color balance. The scales can be positioned along the edge of the original, just outside the image area.

A technique that is very helpful in copying paintings is flashing. Flashing is particularly useful for reducing contrast when copying with color reversal films or color negative camerafilms. KODAK EKTACHROME Duplicating Film 6121 or EKTACHROME Slide Duplicating Film 5071 can be used to achieve a nearly 1:1 contrast ratio. These films are relatively slow, however.

Using Polarizers: Polarizers can be very helpful in copying artwork. Both double polarization and single polarization are helpful techniques. These techniques are explained in the previous section on polarizers. Polarizers, however, must be used with discretion. They will eliminate reflections or the sheen that is sometimes important in the artist's conception of the painting. Double polarized light will eliminate the tiny reflections that occur on the texture of the surface of an oil painting. Removing the reflections may not be desirable if the gloss and texture of the paint are important in the appearance of the painting. The use of polarizers usually increases the contrast and color saturation of the copy. If it is important to maintain these attributes close to those of the original, partial polarization or no polarization can be considered.

Generally, older paintings usually require full polarization but discretion must be used when photographing more recent paintings. On older paintings, the surface varnish may have cracked, and polarization can minimize reflection from the crazing in the copy. Also, texture as part of the artistic presentation is more common in modern work.

Museographics is a studio that copies art objects. Here, proprietor Earl Kage photographs a painting from the Memorial Art Gallery of the University of Rochester using polarizing screens over the lights and a polarizing filter over the camera lens. Note the use of black cloth, drapes, and flats to control reflections.

This copy of the American primitive painting *Pierrepont Edward Lacey* by Noah North was made with quartz lights without polarizers. Note the uneven milkiness of the glaze on the painting surface.

Using double polarization, the surface veiling has been removed, and the contrast has been increased. Flashing could be used to lower the contrast, but Mr. Kage rarely finds it necessary in his work.

Copy by Earl Kage, reproduced with permission of the Memorial Art Gallery of the University of Rochester

84

One-Light Technique for an Impasto Painting

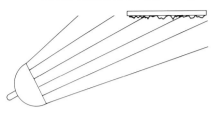

Artists often use the heavy texture of oil paint as part of the artistic experience. Copying the painting with only one light can emphasize the texture. This is called interpretive lighting.

Earl Kage turns a painting on its side and lights from the left, which has become the top of the painting, to show the impasto texture.

When copied with standard two-side lighting, the texture effect of the painting *Plum Island Cottage* by Ward Mann is lost.

More of the effect of a textured painting is retained in the copy when copied with interpretive lighting.

Interpretive Lighting: Occasionally the standard copy lighting arrangement does not illustrate a painting as it was intended to appear. This problem can occur when a three-dimensional effect is present in the painting. When a painter uses the impasto technique, for example, the shadows created by the paint are an important element in producing the illusion of depth. The shadows also create dark areas that the painter uses instead of dark paint. The wrong lighting of a painting of this sort would not display the painting as the artist intended it to be displayed.

The illustrations above show an example of how correct lighting can change the appearance of a painting. In this case the photographer observed that the artist would have had a diffuse overhead light as he painted. (The artist works outdoors.) The photographer then attempted to simulate the lighting conditions for the copy. This was accomplished by turning the painting on its side and lighting it with one light from the "sky" side. The light had to be moved a greater distance from the painting than normal to obtain even illumination.

This concept must be considered when photographing art that is not entirely two-dimensional. The distinction between the art forms of painting and sculpture has become blurred in recent years making this situation more common. In each situation, the photographer must interpret the way in which to light the artwork with sensitivity and skill.

Copy by Earl Kage

To show texture, this painting required a grazing light in addition to the regular copy lights. This light is placed at a narrow angle to the surface plane of the painting. It was positioned so that a ridge of paint on the shoulder of the arm picked up a highlight, which adds sparkle to the copy.

When a painting is mounted in a deep frame, it may be nearly impossible to copy it properly. If permission is granted, the painting can be removed from the frame to be copied. Often the museum staff has an expert to perform this task. If the frame is to appear in the final reproduction, it can be photographed separately to the same scale and the two copies combined for the final reproduction.

Shooting on Location: Unfortunately artwork cannot always be taken to a studio to be photographed. A museum curator is not likely to let a priceless painting be taken to a photographer's studio regardless of the advantages. Also, when a large number of items are to be photographed it is easier to set up on location and photograph there. This saves the cost and risk of transporting a large number of valuable pieces.

Good planning is essential for any kind of location photography. Copying artwork in a museum or institution is no exception. If possible, a preliminary visit to the location is very helpful. During the visit one should take notice of the existing light (artificial or daylight), the room available, the availability of electrical outlets, available power in amperes, and the volume of traffic (human) that the area has. This will help to generate a list of items to bring on location. Such items as extension cords, various focal length lenses, large black flats, and a ladder may be useful.

By checking out the location in advance one can plan to avoid difficult lighting situations. For example, it may be necessary to have a maintenance person turn out the room lights in the area for shooting (but not the electrical outlets). Or it may be necessary to arrange for a piece to be moved if it is located near a window or other source of lighting.

If access to the museum is available at night, copying paintings at that time offers many advantages. There is no daylight coming through windows to contend with (reflections and mixed sources), light sources that might be troublesome can be turned off, and there may be no traffic of visitors to contend with.

Copying Paintings with Infrared and Ultraviolet Radiation: It is occasionally helpful to photograph with infrared or ultraviolet radiation for an investigation or an analysis of a painting. Infrared photography generally refers to the technique of using film that is sensitized into the infrared region of the electromagnetic spectrum for photographing an object. Infrared photography can be used for detecting overpainting or forgeries. The principle is that different pigments may not reflect or transmit infrared radiation the same as visible radiation. As a result, two pigments that appear as identical tones to the eye may record as two very different tones on infrared film. In addition, infrared radiation has the ability to pass through some opaque pigments, making it possible to "see through" several layers of paint. Kodak manufactures infrared film in black and white and color. KODAK High Speed Infrared Film 2481, a black-and-white film, is available in 35mm magazines and long rolls. A similar film, KODAK High Speed Infrared Film 4143 is available in 4 x 5 sheets. KODAK EKTACHROME Infrared Film 2236 is a color reversal film available in 35mm magazines.

When paintings must be copied on location because they are too large or too valuable to be moved, the photographer must move his equipment to the painting—in this case to the Memorial Art Gallery of the University of Rochester. Portable lights, polarizing screens, black flats, and a sturdy tripod are required. Here Earl Kage is photographing the painting shown below.

This film is processed with a Process E-4 which is now only available at a small number of professional labs.

Ultraviolet radiation may also be used to photograph a painting for an investigation. The principle of UV reflection photography is similar to the principle for infrared photography. Two materials (or pigments in this case) may reflect (or transmit) different amounts of ultraviolet radiation yet reflect (or transmit) the same amount of visible light. An ultraviolet source of radiation must be used, and a filter must be used over the lens to eliminate all of the visible light. A normal panchromatic or color film can be used, although color film will generally not be needed. The techniques of copying with infrared and ultraviolet radiation are detailed in the section "Copying with IR and UV Radiation" starting on page 50.

Right: The copy on KODAK EKTACHROME Film that is being made in the illustration above. The painting is a portrait of the Archbishop of Paris Hyacinth Rigand painted in 1731. The room lights have to be turned off for the exposure, and long extension cords were necessary to get power to the lights. The lights had to be brought fairly close to the camera to avoid a shadow of the frame on the painting. Double polarization was used to eliminate the reflection of the light from the painting surface.

Copy by Earl Kage, reproduced with permission of the Memorial Art Gallery of the University of Rochester

COLOR MICROFICHE COPYING

Museums, government agencies, industries, and educational institutions often have many large, detailed color originals such as maps, manuscripts, and records that present preservation and storage problems, as well as photocopying problems.

Two methods have been developed for copying such originals using rolls of 105mm color film at a maximum reduction of 10X (magnification 0.10X) with unusually high image quality. One method uses a standard transparency film, while the other uses a special color negative film.

The processed rolls can be stored, viewed, or printed, and the originals can either be destroyed, reducing the storage area required, or dedicated to long-term, undisturbed storage.

Printing Color Copy Negatives

Color negatives are exposed onto color negative print paper and processed to make color prints. Mass-produced prints are printed from rolls of negatives on computer-controlled printers that expose thousands of prints per hour. The color balance of each negative is measured automatically, and filters in the printer are automatically adjusted to control the color balance of the print. The rolls of exposed paper are processed in continuous-roll processors, and the processed prints are cut automatically. Where color copying is a large-volume business, such equipment is practical for making copy prints.

However, most copying is of lesser volume, and the color negatives are generally enlarged and processed individually.

Color enlargers are usually diffusion-type enlargers with built-in cyan, magenta, and yellow dichroic filtration. The density and color balance of color prints can be controlled by on-easel densitometry or by running tests, evaluating results, and making changes based on the evaluation. This might be called the "trial and error" method.

The primary emphasis of this book is on copying (and duplicating) procedures. If further information is needed on color printing, refer to *Basic Developing, Printing, Enlarging in Color,* Publication AE-13.

DUPLICATING

Introduction to Duplicating

In this book we use the term "duplicating" to mean the reproduction of transparent originals (negatives or transparencies) with photographic materials that yield either film positives or negatives. In the photographic trade, making "dupes" or duplicates usually refers to copying color transparencies with color reversal film. We prefer to use the term duplicating in the broader sense because the techniques and equipment necessary are similar whether negatives, positives, color, or black-and-white images are being reproduced. The section "Duplicating" is divided into two parts: One-Step Duplicating (direct duplicating on reversal films) and Two-Step Duplicating (negative-positive process).

In photographic work it is often necessary or convenient to use a duplicate of an original. Duplicates are expendable, originals are usually not expendable. Valuable photographic originals are generally protected and carefully preserved under dark-storage, temperature-controlled conditions. This applies to both black-and-white and color originals.

There are many reasons why a duplicate negative or transparency may be desirable. For example, by using a duplicate negative to make a large quantity of prints instead of the original negative, the risk of damage to the valuable original is reduced. In this manner, the duplicates serve as working negatives while the original is kept in a safe place. This is a particularly useful procedure for valuable color originals. Long and repeated exposures to intense light sources (as would be encountered in an enlarger or slide projector) can cause fading of the dyes in color negatives and transparencies. By making duplicates, the originals can be kept in cold storage while the more expendable duplicates are used for printing or projection. This procedure is particularly useful for galleries or museums that have large collections of valuable color negatives and transparencies. It is equally useful for the valuable originals of professional and fine-arts photographers.

Duplicates of color transparencies are often needed for slide shows when one slide is to be used several times or when an entire slide show must be shown in several locations at once. It is also useful to duplicate the entire show if it is to be shown repeatedly because fading can occur from repeated projection, and physical damage from repeated handling is also a possibility. Similarly, duplicate negatives can enable the distribution, storage, and simultaneous use of color negatives in many separate geographical locations.

An enlarged duplicate negative is also helpful in reducing printing time and improving sharpness when a very large mural-sized print is required from a small-format negative. It is also useful if the small negative requires retouching.

Museums and other large institutions also find it helpful to have duplicates made of valuable original negatives and transparencies as a precautionary measure in case the original is stolen, accidentally damaged, or destroyed. When an original color negative, transparency, or print is made on a photographic product that is known to fade, or if it has faded, it is useful to make a duplicate on a newer, more stable product to preserve the image or to aid in restoring it.

Making a duplicate is a standard cautionary procedure used by restoration technicians prior to any work on an original. Most restorative techniques involve some degree of risk to the original. A good-quality duplicate provides insurance that if the original is damaged or destroyed during restoration, at least the duplicate will remain.

Also, some restoration techniques make use of a duplicate for the restoration. For example, a duplicate of a damaged negative can be retouched by an artist. The retouched duplicate can then be used to make a print that will be retouched or airbrushed with dyes.

High-quality duplicate transparencies often supplied in multiple copies is a frequent need of any photographer involved in stock photography. In the case of stock agencies, this need to duplicate transparencies may be part of an in-house operation where the volume is much greater.

These examples demonstrate the importance of good-quality duplicates in many areas of photography.

Duplicating techniques range from single-step to elaborate and complex duplicating with masks. Most of the equipment types described earlier are employed providing image-size change, cropping potential, and contrast or density adjustment to suit the reproduction system in use. The potential user should become familiar with the various techniques and materials and then select those that best suit his needs and available equipment.

Whether the duplicating is to be done in black and white or in color, careful preliminary testing is necessary if predictable results are desired.

The chart on the next page graphically illustrates most of the procedures available for making duplicate negatives and transparencies.

Diagram of Duplicating Procedures

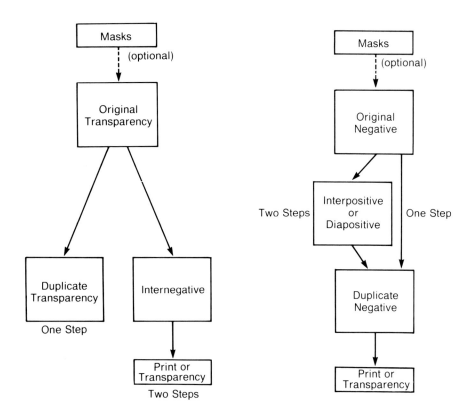

When the original negative has a density range greater than 2.00, the two-step duplicating method can be used.

As with almost any photographic process, a particular set of conditions can produce different results. It is wise to monitor results and make changes to achieve the exact results desired.

Occasionally, tank agitation effects can result in uneven densities in the negatives, especially with relatively short developing times. If sheet film hangers are used for developing, use an oversize tank to minimize these effects. If they still occur, change to tray development.

After fixing and washing the duplicate negatives, they are treated for 3 minutes in the following 1:19 solution of KODAK Rapid Selenium Toner.

Water	950 mL
KODAK Rapid Selenium Toner	50 mL
Solution	1 L

Up to 160 4x5-inch negatives can be treated in a litre of solution. After the treatment, wash the negatives for 30 minutes and dry in the usual manner. Treated duplicate negatives have excellent light- and dark-keeping characteristics. The use of washing aids such as KODAK Hypo Clearing Agent, either before or after treatment, is not recommended. Reduced image stability is very likely to result from the use of washing aids with this film.

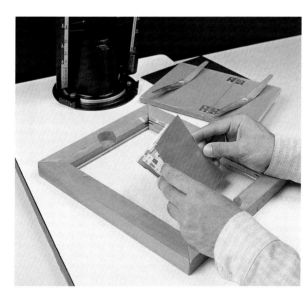

A black-and-white negative is being placed in a contact-printing frame along with a sheet of KODAK Professional B/W Duplicating Film. The enlarger serves as a light source. Of course, this takes place in the dark or under red safelight conditions.

Duplicati...
Transparen...

Duplicating color [...]
accomplished by [...]
parency with a col[...]
reproduction is m[...]

Specialized equi[...]
duplicating. If th[...]
the equipment nee[...]
good results. Whe[...]
ed, the basic equip[...]
camera, is a metho[...]
proportions or gre[...]
the *Equipment* sec[...]
35mm cameras ca[...]
sophistication. T[...]
proportionally. Ex[...]
a prerequisite for [...]
equipment is more[...]
increase speed of o[...]
of the equipment, [...]
the duplicate.

The one piece o[...]
the lens. A lens th[...]
normal distances v[...]
focused at 1:1. F[...]
designed for close[...]
results. More info[...]
and equipment is [...]

Transparencies c[...]
ways. The duplica[...]
tact, with an enlar[...]
that is chosen dep[...]
requirements such[...]
available.

GENERAL PROC[...]
Contact: The me[...]
similar to any othe[...]
to film. In the da[...]
on a sheet of black[...]
transparency is pl[...]
down. A piece of [...]
tion flat during ex[...]
during this operati[...]
duplicate. A printi[...]
convenient to use a[...]
as the light source.[...]
ed by adjusting the[...]
is most often used[...]
parencies.

ONE-STEP DUPLICATING

Duplicating Black-and-White Negatives

There are a number of reasons for making duplicates of black-and-white negatives:

- As a restoration of old negatives on which the nitrate base is deteriorating.

- To change negative size—this may be to enlarge small negatives so that retouching can be done, or reducing old large-size film or glass-plate negatives to a size that is convenient to store and compatible with available equipment.

- To change the contrast (density range) of a negative. Old wet-plate negatives, for example, can have a density range of well over 2.0. These cannot be printed on any current photographic paper. When a duplicate with a lower density range is made, prints on current papers can be made.

- When thousands of prints are to be made, it is often more efficient to multiple-print fewer times than to print more times from a single negative.

- Some laboratories are equipped with automatic contact printers to make large quantities of prints, especially in an 8 x 10-inch size. Negatives of any size can be duplicated by enlarging to make a negative that can be contact-printed.

- Master negatives all alike are sometimes needed as setup or standard negatives in many labs located geographically apart. Such negatives can be made by duplicating an original negative.

Kodak manufactures two black-and-white films used to make general-purpose direct duplicates. That is, the original negative is exposed on the direct-duplicating film, which is developed to produce a negative image. (This is not reversal processing which requires a bleach and a redevelopment.)

KODAK Rapid Process Copy Film is available in 35mm size and KODAK Professional B/W Duplicating Film SO-339 is available in 4 x 5-inch and 8 x 10-inch sheets. Their use is quite similar. KODAK Rapid Process Copy Film is blue-sensitive and can be handled under red, yellow-green, or deep amber safelight filters, while KODAK Professional B/W Duplicating Film SO-339 is orthochromatic and should be handled in darkness or under a 1A (red) safelight only. Both can be exposed in a camera, contact-printed, or exposed in an enlarger. KODAK Professional B/W Duplicating Film SO-339 can be processed in tanks or in trays using KODAK DEKTOL Developer, KODAK Developer DK-50, or DURAFLO chemistry. KODAK Rapid Process Copy Film can be

tank-processed in KODAK Developer DK-50.

In contact printing, it is essential to have good contact between the original negative and the duplicating film to maintain sharpness. Vacuum printing frames are recommended. Spring-back print frames can be used, but care must be taken to ensure good contact. When good contact is obtained, the exposure can be made with a diffuse source such as with a contact printer, with an enlarger used as a light source, or with an exposing light on the ceiling over the exposure area.

When contact printing, Newton's rings often form between the glass of the printing frame and the base of the negative. These may then show up on the negative.

If the negative is to be contact-printed, the glass in the frame can be replaced with anti-Newton ring glass. This has a texture that prevents the rings from forming but leaves a fine pattern on the duplicate negative that can show up on enlargement.

An alternative is the use of a lithographer's offset powder, one example of which is Flo-Mix Non-Offset Powder, available at dealers in graphic arts materials. The powder is very lightly "puffed" onto the clean glass surface with a squeeze bottle. Puff a little into the air to make a light cloud, and pass the glass through this cloud. This technique will almost always eliminate the Newton's-ring problem.

Lithographer's Offset Powder in Squeeze Bottle

POWDER DISPERSED IN AIR

GLASS USED TO CONTACT FILM BASE

The special powder is puffed into the air and a very light coating is allowed to fall on the clean glass.

Anti-Newton Ring Glass Used in Duplicating

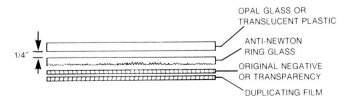

OPAL GLASS OR TRANSLUCENT PLASTIC

ANTI-NEWTON RING GLASS

1/4"

ORIGINAL NEGATIVE OR TRANSPARENCY

DUPLICATING FILM

Use of the spaced diffusing sheet minimizes the texture of the anti-Newton ring glass in the duplicate.

A third approach is to lightly spray the glass with a dilute solution of gum arabic, using an atomizer. A 14% solution of gum arabic can be purchased at art supply stores or drugstores. Add 1/2 ounce of this gum arabic solution to 4 ounces of water, stir, and place in the atomizer spray bottle. The glass is then held horizontally and the spray is aimed upward at the glass so that only a very fine spray reaches the glass. When dry, this coated surface is placed against the base side of the negative. The dry surface can be dusted, but if it requires wet cleaning, wash off the gum arabic, dry the glass, and replace the gum arabic spray.

Contrast is controlled by the degree of development. Shorter developing times result in lower contrast, while longer developing times produce more contrast. The recommended times produce an average contrast.

When using a camera to duplicate negatives, the original is placed on an illuminator and copied by the camera. The copying methods of sizing and focusing on the ground glass are used. The same care to reduce flare and reflections from the surface of the negative must be taken.

Exposure is determined by making a series of test exposures. Because these direct-duplicating films are quite slow (an exposure index of about 0.10 for KODAK Rapid Process Copy Film and about 0.25 for Professional B/W Duplicating Film), exposures are relatively long. Exposure meters cannot be used directly for calculating exposures because they do not usually have settings for such low film speeds. However, by running tests, a correlation between exposure meter readings and the proper exposure can be worked out so that differences in exposure required for negatives of varying densities can be predicted. A method of using a factor of 100X the film speed is described on the instruction sheet packaged with the Rapid Process Copy Film.

When making duplicate negatives that will be used for making prints, expose so that the negative minimum density is about 0.30. This practice minimizes the compression of highlight tones by making sure the toe of the original negative falls above the toe of the duplicating film.

When makin
KODAK Profes
dled in a manne
with photograp
put in the nega
on the easel. Be
sharp as possibl
such as a microg

After the ima
placed on the e
paper. The spee
to a moderate-sp
KODAK EKTA
is made. A final
results of the tes

With these tw
produces light re
dark results.

Control of Con
duplicate negativ
Duplicating Fil
density range. T
change and mak

A negative wi
considered norn
enlarger. The fol
point for making

Characteristic C
Du

Process: Tra
70°F (21°

KODAK Developer	Development Time (Minutes) at 7	
	Tray*	La
DEKTOL (1:1)	2	
DK-50	—	

*With continuous agitation.
†With manual agitation at 1-minute intervals.

The development times in the table are starting-point recommend
Professional B/W Duplicating Film. Times can be varied to produce the
the duplicate.

Projection: Duplicates can also be exposed with an enlarger by projection. The exposing technique is similar to making prints except a transparency is placed in the negative carrier instead of a negative, and duplicating film is placed on the easel instead of photographic paper. The filter pack can be adjusted with dichroic filters if the enlarger is so equipped, or with KODAK Color Printing (CP) Filters in the filter drawer of the enlarger. If filters must be used in front of the lens of the enlarger, KODAK Color Compensating (CC) Filters should be used.

Camera: Same-size duplicates of small-format transparencies are most often exposed in a camera and a camera-lens arrangement that will permit 1:1 on-film magnification. The equipment available for this task can be very specialized or merely a rudimentary adaptation of a simple camera. The basic requirements and procedures remain the same. A device for holding and illuminating the transparency parallel to the camera's film plane is necessary when making duplicates with a camera. The light source should have some method of diffusing the light before it strikes the transparency. The light source must provide even illumination across the transparency. A place for inserting filters is also necessary.

In all cases, the transparency should be cleaned with compressed ionized air or an antistatic device prior to duplicating. Oil or stubborn dirt can often be removed using film cleaner* and a cotton swab. Fingerprints cannot always be removed by cleaning. Using a diffuse light source will help minimize all of these problems.

When focusing close-up equipment at distances near 1:1, the lens movement changes image size while the movement of the camera body changes the focus. This is the opposite of the procedure used in normal picture-taking.

When the slide or transparency is positioned for copying, it should be oriented so that the emulsion is facing away from the camera so that the duplicate is not laterally reversed when compared to the original.

For optimum sharpness in duplicating 35mm slides, the originals can be mounted in glass slide mounts. This will help keep the originals flat. Flatness is important at close-focusing distances where depth-of-field is limited.

A color reversal duplicating film is preferred for copying transparencies instead of a general-purpose camera film. A duplicating film produces lower contrast and has a characteristic curve shape that is designed for good tone reproduction when copying transparencies. These films produce better highlight and shadow tone reproduction in duplicates than do camera films. See illustrations on pages 98 and 99.

It is essential that the proper light source be used with each film product. The chart on page 96 gives the light sources that are intended for each film product.

The filtration necessary for each film varies with the type of film that is used as an original. A different filter pack is usually required for duplicating originals on KODACHROME Film than for EKTACHROME Film. The filter pack requirements are also different for older films of the same type (KODACHROME Film, Process K-12, EKTACHROME Film, Process E-4, etc.).

These differences can be minimized by using a KODAK Infrared Cutoff Filter No. 304 between the light source and the transparency. This filter should be positioned perpendicular to the light source with the coated side facing the bulb. The filter should be in front of any diffusion material, nearest to the light source.

A disadvantage of using this filter is that the intensity of the light is reduced greatly. This might require excessively long exposures in some situations. Another disadvantage is that the color reproduction may not be as good as it would be using a normal filter pack. There can be red contrast difficulties.

Adjusting the Filter Pack: Critical color evaluation of slides should be made with a projector if the slides are to be projected. A standard 5000 K illuminator with a CRI rating of at least 95 is used for evaluating color balance, particularly if the transparencies are to be reproduced photomechanically. Fluorescent tubes that have an equivalent color balance of 5000 K can be purchased for light boxes.

5000 K illumination with a high color rendering index is an industry standard for evaluating color by photographers, printers, and photographic manufacturers.

*Do not use motion picture film cleaners which contain a lubricant.

The illustration above was made directly from a slide on POLACHROME Film. It was reproduced dark to show its original appearance. Such slides can be reproduced to a normal density even though their densities are considerably higher than that of slides on KODACHROME or EKTACHROME Films.

This illustration was made of a duplicate of the slide made on POLACHROME Film. The duplicate was made on KODAK EKTACHROME Slide Duplicating Film. Such duplicate slides can be intermixed with other slides on transparency films for normal projection brightness.

Duplicating Slides Made on POLAROID POLACHROME Film: POLACHROME Film is an additive film rather than subtractive like KODACHROME and EKTACHROME Film. As a result, the slides made on POLACHROME Film are much darker than conventional slides. This makes them unsuitable for regular projection intermixed with regular slides. However, duplicate slides can be made from POLACHROME Film slides that have the same density characteristics as normal slides.

When duplicating on KODAK EKTACHROME Slide Duplicating Film, POLACHROME Film slides require about 3 stops more or 8X the exposure for regular slides. In addition, they require a filtration of about CC25G greater than that used for duplicating EKTACHROME Film slides. Properly balanced and exposed duplicates make quite good slides for projection.

Duplicating Color Negatives

The simplest and most direct way to duplicate a color negative is to print it on a color reversal film. KODAK EKTACHROME Duplicating Film 6121 (sheets) and KODAK EKTACHROME Slide Duplicating Film 5071 (rolls) are excellent films for this purpose.

Duplicating films generally make better duplicates than camera films because their sensitometric characteristics provide better contrast and tone reproduction for this purpose.

The same general procedure that is used for duplicating color transparencies is used for duplicating color negatives with KODAK EKTACHROME Duplicating Films. The original negative is treated as if it were a transparency to be duplicated. The same filtration that is used for making duplicate color transparencies should be used as a starting point in making duplicate color negatives. To determine if the color balance is acceptable, a color print must be made. The color balance can also be evaluated on a densitometer or a color analyzer. The duplicate should have similar red, green, and blue density ranges as the original (measured with Status M filtration). Most areas in the duplicate should have densities about 0.10 higher than the original, in order to get the tone reproduction up off the toe of the duplicating film.

An exposure adjustment of one-half to one full stop underexposure is necessary when duplicating color negatives with this method. This puts most of the tones of the reproduction on the relatively straight portion of the characteristic curve of the duplicating film. By placing the reproduction on the straight line portion of the curve the duplicate will reproduce the original almost tone for tone.

Some loss of color saturation can be expected, but as the illustration above shows, the loss is minimal. Underexposing as recommended above will help to reduce any loss of color saturation.

When a small-sized duplicate negative is to be used for making enlarged color prints, the duplicate negative should be enlarged to about three times the size of the original negative to maintain about the same visual graininess as in a print from the original.

Although the grain on EKTACHROME Duplicating Film is extremely fine, when duplicate negatives are made the same size there is an enhancement of graininess. But when the duplicate negative is enlarged several times, the enlarged grain of the original negative image becomes large compared to that of the duplicating film and the effect is eliminated.

If the original negative is quite contrasty, a positive contrast-reducing mask can be made to fit in register with the original. The technique for making contrast-reducing masks can be found on page 108.

Another method of making duplicate color negatives is to neutralize the orange-colored minimum density with filtration. Complete neutralizing may require CC90C + CC30M filtration. If this leads to excessively long exposures, as little as CC50C can be used with adequate results. With dichroic filters in an enlarger head, less filtration may be required.

Both methods, duplicating as is and duplicating with neutralizing filtration, are being used successfully. If you have any quantity of color negative duplication to do, you might try both methods and compare results.

This illustration was made from a color print made from the original color negative.

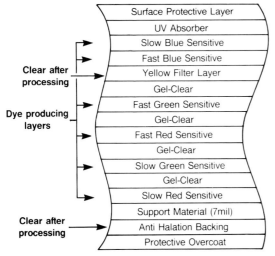

Layer Thicknesses not to scale

KODAK Photographic Step Tablets No. 2 and No. 3 are recommended for large transparency reproduction, while the smaller No. 1A can be cut and mounted in a slide mount to monitor the reproduction of slides. Photographic step tablet No. 2 can be cut and realigned when internegatives are being made from intermediate-size transparencies (6 x 4.5 to 6 x 7 cm transparencies). The illustration shows how this is done. In addition to making the step tablet a convenient size, this realignment procedure helps to reduce the effect of nonuniform illumination on the test exposures.

It is also useful to make a test transparency using a 35mm camera with a metering system by copying a gray scale and color patches on KODACHROME or EKTACHROME Film as a visual check. Reproducing this via internegative film gives a visual check as described on page 72 for making copy negatives from color prints.

Making Internegatives with an Enlarger: Using the enlarger to make internegatives is quite a common practice because all of the equipment for the procedure is usually in place for making color prints. It offers the opportunity to make almost any size internegative as well. A color enlarger with dial filtration is a most convenient method, and the same on-easel color densitometry can be adapted for exposure and color balance control. If care is taken, there is somewhat less of a problem with dust than with contact printing because if a glassless carrier is used, there are fewer surfaces to keep clean and dirt-free.

The basic procedure is the same as making a color print. The transparency is placed in the enlarger and the image sized and focused on the easel. If the transparency is placed emulsion side up, the negative image will have the correct orientation. However, because contact internegatives have reversed images, they must be printed reversed as well. A grain focuser is a help in achieving exact focus. The enlarger lens is stopped down to its sharpest aperture—usually ƒ/11 or ƒ/8. The internegative film is placed on the easel for the exposure (in total darkness, of course).

The copying procedure is the same as conventional copying except that the transparencies are placed on an illuminator in place of the copyboard and completely masked with black paper. The illuminator should have a 3200 K balance. Fluorescent lamps are generally unsuitable sources for color applications and are not recommended.

A particular problem can be reflections off the surface of the transparencies. This can be controlled by turning off all the room illumination and by using a deep black mask of cardboard covered with black velvet in front of the camera. A circular hole is cut in the mask for the camera lens.

It is usually important to get the highest degree of sharpness possible in the copy internegatives. A magnifier should be used when focusing with a ground glass. The best aperture of the copy lens should be used. This usually is a middle aperture. Larger apertures (lower ƒ-numbers) may not give maximum aberration correction and limit depth-of-field, which can lead to focus errors. Using smaller apertures (higher ƒ-numbers) introduces diffraction, which lowers sharpness. Keeping the copy lens clean aids both sharpness and tone reproduction.

Photographic step tablets are used to monitor the making of internegatives by all three methods.

111

Please refer to the instruction sheets packaged with the film for balancing instructions. If you have previously used KODAK VERICOLOR Internegative Film, Type 2/4114, use your most recent exposure time and filter pack as a starting point.

Making a Test Exposure: The recommended basic exposure time is 10 seconds. The illumination at the exposure (film) plane should be about 3 footcandles for this exposure time.

To determine this level for contact printing or enlarging, place a piece of white paper in the exposing plane (on the enlarging easel) and adjust the light level by raising and lowering the enlarger and adjusting the f-number until a reflection exposure meter reading of 1/8 sec at f/5.6 is achieved with the film speed setting placed at ISO 400. There should be no filtration of the light when this measurement is made. This indicates an illuminance of 3 footcandles.

The enlarger, illuminator, or other exposure lamp should be equipped with a heat-absorbing glass and a UV filter such as the KODAK WRATTEN Filter No. 2B. The starting filter pack recommendations call for a filtration of 30M + 30Y, either as a setting on the enlarger dials or with CP or CC filters.

The intended exposure range for KODAK Commercial Internegative Film 4325/5325 is between 1/10 second to 30 seconds. Because of changes in the speed in the three dye image layers that result from exposure time changes due to the reciprocity characteristics of the film, it is advisable to keep the exposure time as close to 10 seconds as practical. Changes in exposure time may require changes in color balance for optimum internegatives. With contact printing, using an enlarger as a light source, changing the enlarger height and the lens f-number can almost always provide the right level of illumination to keep a 10-second exposure time. With an exposure lamp, raising and lowering the lamp adjusts the illumination level.

However, when using the copying techniques with an illuminator, changing the illumination level to attain a 10-second exposure at the sharpest f-number of the copying lens may be difficult. A variable transformer cannot be used with the illuminator lamps to change the light intensity because changing the voltage changes the color temperature, which must remain constant. One solution is to use higher or lower wattage bulbs to shorten or lengthen the exposure time to 10 seconds. In the extreme, more bulbs can be added to the illuminator or subtracted from it to obtain the correct exposure time. Sheets of KODAK WRATTEN Neutral Density Filter No. 96 in varying densities can be used to lower the light level. Each 0.10 density lowers the exposure by 1/3 stop. A 0.30 filter lowers the exposure by 1 stop. Sheets of KODAK Neutral Density Filter are catalog-listed up to 125 mm (5 inches) square and can be special-ordered up to 350 mm (14 inches) square. Once the exposure time of 10 seconds is achieved, however, it should become a constant for all transparencies. Slight changes in aperture are used to compensate for light and dark transparencies.

In making a test, the film step tablet chosen earlier is imaged on the film. In contact printing, the step tablet is placed in contact with the internegative film. In copying, the step tablet is placed on the illuminator and masked with black paper. In enlarging, the step tablet is placed in the negative carrier and completely masked.

Dial the starting filter pack (or place the filters) in the enlarger, on the copy lens, or on the exposure lamp. Put a sheet of film in place and give it a 10-second exposure. Process the film in a well-controlled Process C-41.

With KODAK VERICOLOR Internegative Film 4112: Proceed to "Controlling the Internegative."

With KODAK Commercial Internegative Film: Use a densitometer to check the overall exposure level. Set the densitometer to Status M and make sure it is calibrated. Read and record the red, green, and blue densities of Step 3 of the step-tablet image on the internegative film.

Compare your readings to the following:
Red   1.30 to 1.50
Green   1.50 to 1.70
Blue   1.90 to 2.10

If the densities of Step 3 fall below these ranges, increase the exposure time or open the lens aperture the equivalent of one f-stop. Expose and process another internegative and check the densities.

If the densities of Step 3 are above these ranges, decrease the exposure time or close the lens aperture the equivalent of one f-stop. Expose and process another internegative and check the densities.

Note: If the red density is within the acceptable range, but the green or blue density is not, you can control the green and blue exposures individually, as follows: Increase green exposure by subtracting 30M from the filter pack or decrease it by adding 30M. Increase blue exposure by subtracting 30Y or decrease it by adding 30Y.

When all three densities of Step 3 fall within the acceptable ranges, read and record the red, green, and blue Status M densities of all the steps of the image. You can now select the evaluation method you want to use.

KODAK Photographic Step Tablets

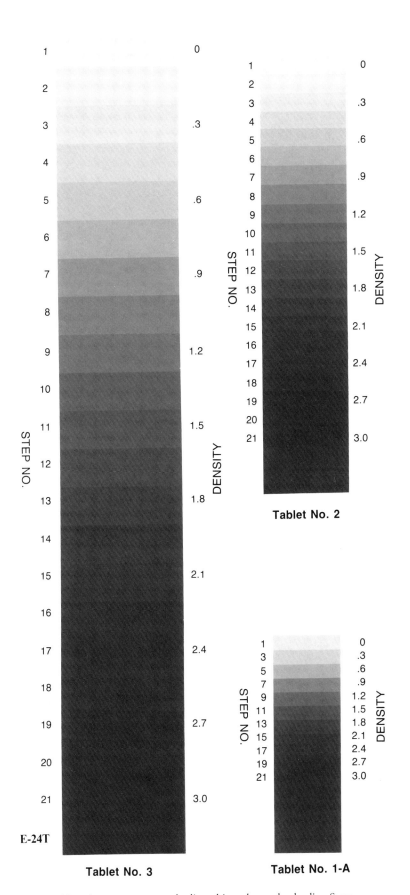

Tablet No. 3

E-24T

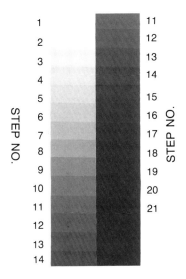

Tablet No. 2
Cut and realigned to reduce effect of nonuniformity of illuminant.

Tablet No. 1-A

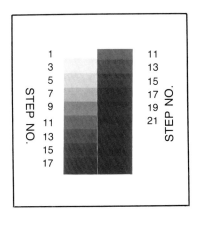

Tablet No. 1-A
Mounted with steps paired to reduce effect of nonuniformity of the illuminant.

Note that some steps are duplicated in order to closely align Steps 3 with 13, 5 with 15, etc. Closely aligning the pairs of steps is recommended in order to place them in the same area of illumination.

Controlling the Internegative

As mentioned earlier in connection with making copy internegatives of reflection originals, there are several methods of controlling the reproduction by the internegative film. The first to be discussed is the density-difference method.

DENSITY-DIFFERENCE BALANCING METHOD FOR KODAK COMMERCIAL INTERNEGATIVE FILM 4325/5325

This evaluation method involves making exposure adjustments based on the differences between two points on the characteristic curves of the step-tablet image. The goal of this method is for acceptable values of all three (red, green, and blue) density differences to fall in the high-density/low-density Step Pair 3/13.

To do this in as few trials as possible, calculate the density differences (DDs) for the first seven step pairs by subtracting the densities of the low-density (LD) steps from the densities of the corresponding high-density (HD) steps.

Important: Be sure to use Status M density values for the density-difference method of balancing, not printing-density values as for the full-curve-plotting method.

Density-Difference Aims for 4325/5325 Film

Red DD	Blue DD	Green DD
0.66 ± .03	0.66 ± .03	0.85 ± .03

Referring to the density-difference worksheet, find the step pairs having density differences that are closest to the recommended aims. Again, the goal of this evaluation method is to have all three acceptable density differences fall within Step Pair 3/13.

Make filter pack adjustments based on which step pair is closest to the density-difference aims. Apply the cyan filter for the red step pair, the magenta filter for the green step pair, and the yellow filter for the blue step pair.

Step Pair Closest to Aim	Filter Change
1/11	-30
2/12	-15
3/13	None
4/14	+15
5/15	+30
6/16	+45

Calculate the new filter pack by adding or subtracting the appropriate filter changes. Cancel out any neutral density in your filter pack by subtracting a common density value from all three filters.

Filter Pack Calculation

	Cyan	Magenta	Yellow
1. Starting pack	0	+30	+30
2. Filter change from above	+15	+30	+45
3. Resulting filtration	+15	+60	+75
4. Neutral density elimination	-15	-15	-15
5. New filter pack	0	+45	+60

If you cancel neutral density out of your filter pack, exposure compensation may be necessary. Every 15 points of filtration equals 1/2 stop of exposure; 30 points is a full stop.

Expose another sheet of film using the new filter pack. Process the film and evaluate the step tablet using the density-difference method. Density differences of the red, green, and blue readings should meet aims at Step Pair 3/13. Then make an internegative from a reference transparency, print the internegative, and evaluate the print to verify the filter pack.

DENSITY-DIFFERENCE BALANCING METHOD FOR KODAK VERICOLOR INTERNEGATIVE FILM 4112

As with making copy internegatives of color prints, the density-difference method of balancing requires less time but may not give as much information as the curve comparison method.

Example of a Density-Difference Worksheet

Status M Reading	Density	High-Density/Low-Density Step Pairs of Step-Tablet Image						
		1/11	2/12	3/13	4/14	5/15	6/16	7/17
Red	HD	1.61	1.44	1.32	1.21	1.11	1.02	.95
	−LD	−.70	−.65	−.60	−.56	−.51	−.47	−.43
	DD	.91	.79	.72	.65	.60	.55	.52
Green	HD	2.10	2.03	1.95	1.84	1.71	1.60	1.49
	−LD	−1.19	−1.13	−1.08	−1.03	−.98	−.93	−.90
	DD	.91	.90	.87	.81	.73	.67	.59
Blue	HD	2.53	2.42	2.31	2.15	1.98	1.84	1.71
	−LD	−1.40	−1.34	−1.29	−1.23	−1.16	−1.09	−1.04
	DD	1.13	1.08	1.02	.92	.82	.75	.67

This method can be used for balancing the 4112 film when using the appropriate density-difference tables. For detailed instruction for the density-difference procedure, please refer to the balancing procedures given in KODAK Data Release E-24S, *Balancing KODAK VERICOLOR Internegative Film 4112.*

When the film is dry, measure the red, green, and blue densities of the No. 3 step as imaged on the film. (See illustration for locating the steps.)

The densities of Step 3 should not exceed these values.

Red Filter   1.50 (Cyan Emulsion Layer)
Green Filter   1.90 (Magenta Emulsion Layer)
Blue Filter   2.30 (Yellow Emulsion Layer)

If any of the densities exceeds these values, measure the No. 5 step. Note that only the odd-numbered steps are used. These are 0.30 or 1 stop apart on the original step tablet. Usually the No. 3 or No. 5 steps will meet the criteria. If not, make a new test film giving it 2 stops less exposure.

Example Density-Difference Calculations

Density	R	G	B
Step 3	1.10	1.50	2.11
Step 13	0.51	0.90	1.27
DD Values	0.59	0.60	0.84

You have now located a step where the red, green, and blue densities do not exceed the values shown above. Count to a step number that is 10 greater than this step. If it is No. 3, count to Step No. 13. If it is No. 5, count to Step No. 15.

Measure the densities of this step.

With a 21-step tablet, you will end up with the densities of a pair of steps that are 10 steps apart, such as 3 and 13 or 5 and 15. With an 11-step tablet, the pair of steps will be 5 steps apart, although the numbers will be 10 apart because the steps are all odd-numbered.

Finding the Density Differences: Density difference is found by subtracting the smaller value from the larger value. As an example, let us use the density values shown above for Steps No. 3 and No. 13. The density-difference calculation is shown.

Density-Difference Aims for 4112 Film

Red DD	Green DD	Blue DD
0.63 ± .03	0.73 ± .03	0.79 ± .03

Note that the aim density differences are not the same for the three layers.

The reason for these differences is that the transmissions of the Status M filters used to measure the color densities do not exactly match the color sensitivities of the paper layers on which the negatives are printed. The DD aims given are Status M aims that match the contrast as the paper sees the dyes in the color film. This situation is not limited to color internegative films and is equally true with color negative camera films.

These density differences are designed to fit the averages of the three image layers of KODAK EKTACOLOR Paper. Aims may be different for other color print materials.

Also, the aims should be considered starting points that may have to be adjusted for any particular set of circumstances. When you have reached the aims with a test internegative, this negative should be printed, and a neutral balance for the midtones should be achieved. If the highlight and shadow tones are also neutral, the DD aims are satisfactory for your conditions. If however, there is a color shift from the highlights to the shadows, the aims need to be changed because the internegative is out of balance.

To correct the imbalance, subtract the color of the highlight tinge from the filter pack. If for example, the highlights have a tinge of yellow, subtract yellow filtration from the pack. There is a discussion of this procedure on page 72 in the section entitled "Visual Check of Color Internegatives." The testing continues until a test print shows a neutral gray scale along its entire length. The density differences of this internegative become your new set of DD aims.

Finding a New Filter Pack for the Density Differences: The table on page 116 is used to find the filter pack changes required to bring the negative density differences close to the aim values on the next test internegative.

Look for the red, green, and blue density differences in the DD columns. The recommended filter change is found in the next column.

Where the red filter density is 0.59, as in our example, the recommended cyan filter change is -CC13. The recommended filter changes are added to the original filter pack, which was 30M + 30Y (the starting pack when you do not have previous filter settings).

Example of Filter Pack Correction

Status M Filter	DD	Filter Pack Change
Red	0.59	-13 Cyan
Green	0.66	-21 Magenta
Blue	0.84	+10 Yellow

Note that when the change is minus (-), "adding" the change really means subtracting it from the pack value.

Filter Changes Based on Density Differences of KODAK VERICOLOR Internegative Film

Red DD	Cyan Filter Change	Green DD	Magenta Filter Change	Blue DD	Yellow Filter Change
		Under 0.60	−45	Under 0.66	−45
		0.60	−45	0.66	−45
		0.61	−40	0.67	−42
Under 0.53	−45	0.62	−36	0.68	−38
0.53	−45	0.63	−32	0.69	−34
0.54	−36	0.64	−28	0.70	−30
0.55	−30	0.65	−24	0.71	−26
0.56	−25	0.66	−21	0.72	−22
0.57	−21	0.67	−18	0.73	−18
0.58	−17	0.68	−15	0.74	−15
0.59	−13	0.69	−12	0.75	−12
0.60	−10	0.70	−09	0.76	−08
0.61	−07	0.71	−06	0.77	−05
0.62	−04	0.72	−03	0.78	−03
AIM: 0.63	00	0.73	00	0.79	00
0.64	+02	0.74	+02	0.80	+02
0.65	+05	0.75	+05	0.81	+04
0.66	+08	0.75	+07	0.82	+06
0.67	+11	0.77	+10	0.83	+08
0.68	+13	0.78	+13	0.84	+10
0.69	+15	0.79	+15	0.85	+12
0.70	+17	0.80	+17	0.86	+14
0.71	+19	0.81	+19	0.87	+16
0.72	+21	0.82	+21	0.88	+18
0.73	+23	0.83	+23	0.89	+20
0.74	+25	0.84	+25	0.90	+22
0.75	+27	0.85	+27	0.91	+24
0.76	+29	0.86	+29	0.92	+26
0.77	+31	0.87	+31	0.93	+28
0.78	+33	0.88	+33	0.94	+29
0.79	+35	0.89	+35	0.95	+31
0.80	+37	0.90	+36	0.96	+33
0.81	+38	0.91	+38	0.97	+34
0.82	+40	0.92	+40	0.98	+36
0.83	+42	0.93	+42	0.99	+37
0.84	+44	0.94	+43	1.00	+39
0.85	+45	0.95	+45	1.01	+41
Over 0.85	+45	Over 0.95	+45	1.02	+42
				1.03	+44
				1.04	+45
				Over 1.04	+45

Exposure Change Table

For Plus Values		For Minus Values	
If the neutral density added in line 4 is:	Multiply the internegative exposure by:	If the neutral density subtracted in line 4 is:	Multiply the internegative exposure by:
0.00	1.00	−0.00	1.00
+0.02 (no change)	1.06	−0.02 (no change)	0.96
+0.04	1.12	−0.04	0.92
+0.06	1.17	−0.06	0.88
+0.08	1.23	−0.08	0.84
+0.10 (+ 1/3 stop)	1.28	−0.10 (− 1/3 stop)	0.80
+0.12	1.34	−0.12	0.77
+0.14	1.40	−0.14	0.73
+0.16	1.46	−0.16	0.69
+0.18	1.51	−0.18	0.65
+0.20 (+ 2/3 stop)	1.57	−0.20 (− 2/3 stop)	0.61
+0.22	1.66	−0.22	0.60
+0.24	1.74	−0.24	0.58
+0.26	1.82	−0.26	0.55
+0.28	1.90	−0.28	0.53
+0.30 (+ 1 stop)	2.00	−0.30 (− 1 stop)	0.50

Filter Pack Calculation

	Cyan	Magenta	Yellow
1. Starting pack	0	+30	+30
2. Filter change from above	-13	-21	+10
3. Resulting filtration	-13	+9	+40
4. Neutral density elimination	+13	+13	+13
5. New filter pack	0	+22	+53

If CC filters are used over a lens, as when enlarging with a black-and-white enlarger or when copying a transparency, as few filters as possible (not more than three) should be used to avoid possible loss of contrast and sharpness. This problem does not arise with enlargers in which filtration is dialed.

Calculating Exposure Changes for the New Pack:
The amount of exposure change is determined by how much the neutral density is changed in the calculations above. If neutral density is added, as in our example, the exposure must be increased for the next exposure on the internegative film. If neutral density is subtracted, the exposure is decreased.

The table on page 116 can be used to calculate the amount of exposure change. Look up the + or - neutral density change in the proper column, and note the exposure change in stops or in a factor by which to change the exposure time.

In our example, the neutral density change was +0.25, so the left columns are used. The value shows a change of +1 stop, which means opening up the lens by one stop, or multiplying the exposure time by a factor of between 1.74 and 1.82, or 1.78. If the original time is 10 seconds, the changed time would be 18 seconds. The aperture change is preferable because 18 seconds is nearly twice the preferred 10-second exposure.

If the neutral density change value had been a –0.10, for example, then the lens is stopped down by 1/3 stop or the exposure time is multiplied by 0.80. The 10-second exposure would become 10 x 0.80 = 8 seconds.

In practice when copying or enlarging, it is wise to adjust in such a way that the exposure time stays as near to 10 seconds as practical, and the lens stays in its middle *f*-number range for maximum sharpness.

The scale shown on the bottom of page 118 displays a 1/6-stop increment *f*-number series. Each 1/6 stop is equivalent to a 0.05 neutral density change.

Partial-stop aperture changes are equivalent to the following exposure time factor changes:

Aperture Change

Increase	Exposure Time Factor
1/6 Stop	1.12X
1/3 Stop	1.26X
1/2 Stop	1.41X
1 Stop	2.00X

Decrease	Exposure Time Factor
1/6 Stop	0.89X
1/3 Stop	0.79X
1/2 Stop	0.71X
1 Stop	0.50X

Internegatives made by contact should be enlarged with the base side toward the lens to obtain the correct image orientation in the print.

MAKING A PRINT

When the internegative meets the aims, a test print is made that is balanced to the middle gray. If the gray scale is neutral, a balance has been achieved.

If the highlights have a tinge of color, a correction needs to be made. The same procedure of correcting is used as if making a copy internegative of a color print. See the discussion on page 70.

It should be noted that a print of the step scale that is neutral from black to white does not necessarily mean the internegatives are exactly balanced. The step scale is a black-and-white silver image while the transparency is a dye image, and the two image materials do not always reproduce exactly the same. The final judgment must therefore be made on the print reproduction of the transparency.

There are several reasons why you may need slightly different density-difference aims than those given above. One is flare. If lens coatings cause "colored" flare, then the image formed by that lens may have a different exposure range in one color than another. If a transparency has predominance of one strong color, the flare will be colored. This causes the same effect. Another reason is that paper may vary slightly, box to box, and a slight shift in the aims may be needed to adjust for normal manufacturing tolerance. Yet another reason is that color processes are not identical, and adjustment must be made for the particular process being used. Print viewing and evaluation will indicate the need for aim changes.

If a transparency is very contrasty or very low in contrast, all three aims can be lowered or raised to obtain a normal-contrast internegative. A test can be run using a 1/2-stop change in exposure to find how much the aims need to be changed.

Curve-Plotting Method of Internegative Control

Curve-plotting is an alternative method of controlling the balance and exposure of color internegatives made from transparencies. This method takes longer than the density-difference method but provides the user with more detailed information about the contrast relationships between the individual red-, green-, and blue-sensitive emulsion layers of the internegative film. A description of the curve-plotting method of internegative control follows.

Overview: The internegative film is exposed to a photographic step tablet as described on page 112. The 1-A step tablet may be cut and mounted in a standard 35mm slide mount as described in Publications E-24S, *Balancing KODAK VERICOLOR Internegative Film 4112*, and E-225T, *Balancing KODAK Commercial Internegative Film 4325/5325*. The exposure conditions are the same as for the density-difference method. After exposure, the internegative is processed in a well-controlled Process C-41.

Measuring the Internegative: Once the transparency is processed, the red, green, and blue Status M densities of the 21 steps of the exposed silver tablet are measured and recorded. The measured densities of the individual steps are needed for the balancing step, and Status M densitometry is required.

Plotting: The Status M densities recorded earlier are then plotted on *KODAK Curve-Plotting Graph Paper*, Publication E-64. This paper is thin and translucent for easy comparison on an illuminator.

With KODAK VERICOLOR Internegative Film 4112, plot the red, blue, and green curves on a single sheet of graph paper. The lower curve is the red curve, the middle curve is the green, and the upper curve is the blue. If KODAK Commercial Internegative Film is used, plot each curve on a separate sheet of graph paper.

The density of each step is plotted as a point above the appropriate step number in Scale A on the plotting paper. When all the steps are plotted, each curve is drawn by connecting the plotted points of each color. Draw the connecting lines with a French curve to provide a smooth curve, and as the illustration shows, three curves result.

Note that each of the curves should have a straight-line section to the left and an upward sweep to the right. It is this upward sweep that provides the highlight tone separation needed for the best tone reproduction. (See page 4.)

INTERPRETING THE CURVES
KODAK VERICOLOR INTERNEGATIVE FILM:
The curves from the Status M densities are then compared to the reference curves published in E-24S. The comparison is done by superimposing the plotted curves on top of the reference curves. Filter pack and exposure data are then determined by shifting each internegative curve to obtain the best possible match with the appropriate reference curve. The internegative is correctly balanced and exposed when the red, green, and blue curves match the appropriate reference curves.

KODAK Commercial Internegative Film: Place the sheet of graph paper with the red curve on a light table and put the sheet with the green curve on top of it. Keep the horizontal and vertical axes of the two graphs parallel and shift the green curve until it is superimposed on the red curve. The most critical area to match is between Steps 2 and 10 on the red curve. Note the amount of offset. Then evaluate the blue curve the same way.

The amount of offset required to match the curves indicates the amount of filtration needed to balance the internegative. See the Legend in the lower right corner of the Reference Curves on page 119. The direction of the shift indicates whether filtration is added or subtracted. If the top curve is shifted to the left of the red curve, subtract filtration. If it is to the right, add filtration. Set the new filter pack and make another exposure of the step tablet.

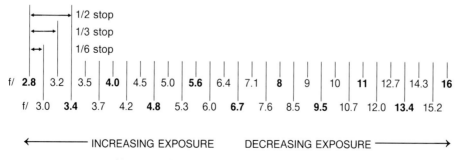

Change in Exposure by Aperture (f-Number)

Upper row bold figures are usual marked full stops.
Lower row bold figures are usual marked half stops.

KODAK Curve Plotting Graph Paper

KODAK Internegative (Transmission) Reference Curves
(Status M Readings)

Step	Red	Green	Blue
1	1.41	1.90	2.30
2	1.28	1.76	2.16
3	1.17	1.63	2.02
4	1.08	1.52	1.91
5	1.00	1.42	1.81
6	0.93	1.33	1.71
7	0.86	1.25	1.62
8	0.80	1.18	1.54
9	0.75	1.12	1.47
10	0.70	1.06	1.40
11	0.65	1.00	1.34
12	0.60	0.94	1.28
13	0.55	0.88	1.22
14	0.50	0.82	1.16
15	0.45	0.77	1.10
16	0.40	0.72	1.04
17	0.36	0.67	0.98
18	0.32	0.62	0.93
19	0.28	0.57	0.88
20	0.24	0.52	0.83
21	0.20	0.47	0.78

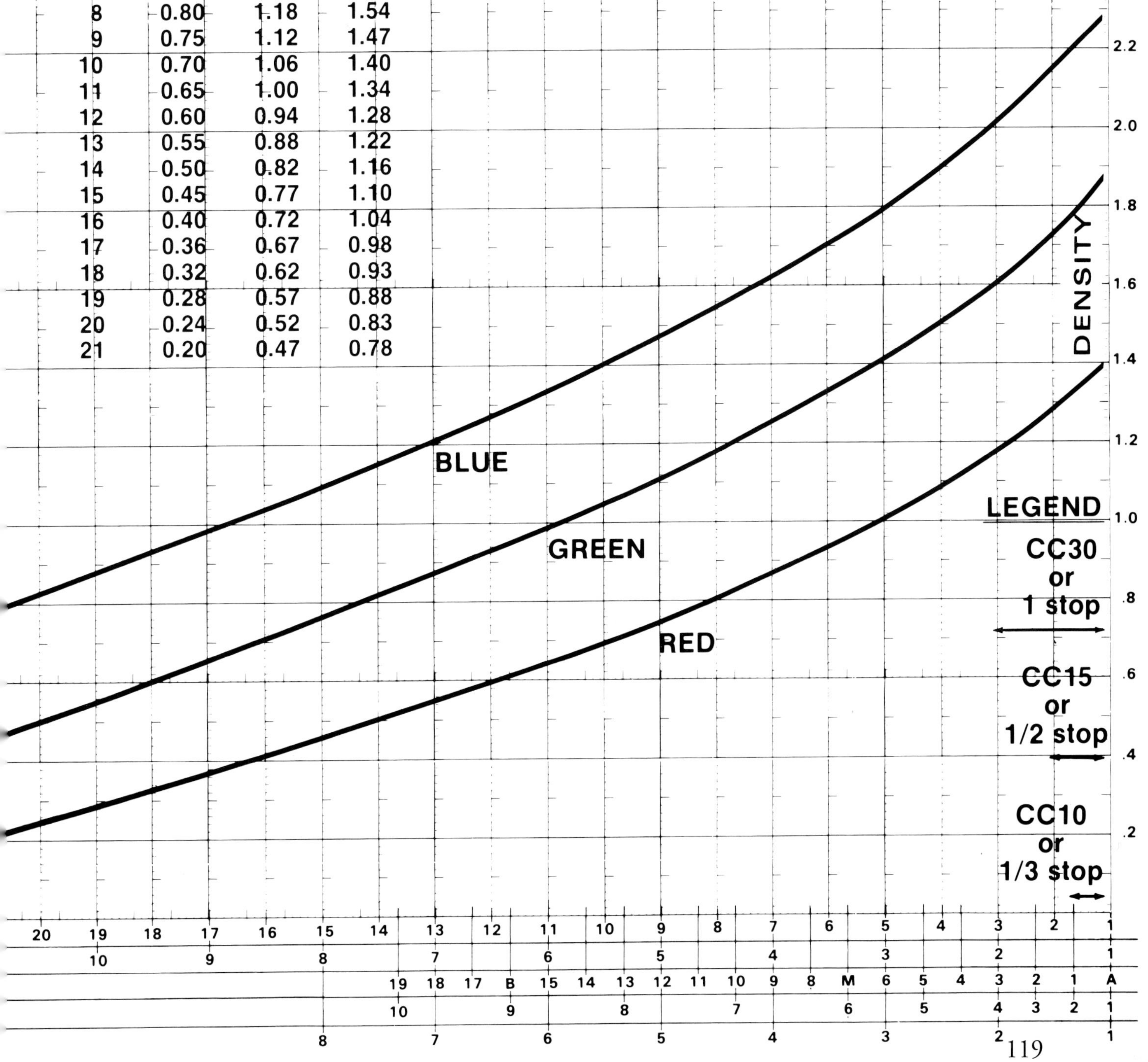

No. _____   Date _____

BLUE

GREEN

RED

DENSITY

LEGEND

CC30
or
1 stop

CC15
or
1/2 stop

CC10
or
1/3 stop

119

What the Curves Tell You: A properly exposed and balanced internegative will make a print with a gray scale which is balanced for color along its entire tonal scale and which has proper tone separation in the highlight steps. A balanced but overexposed negative will print a balanced gray scale but will have too much highlight tone separation and too little shadow tone separation. Conversely, an underexposed internegative will have too little highlight separation and will give a generally low-contrast print. Any imbalance in the internegative is indicated by difficulty in printing a gray scale that is neutral from highlight to shadow. If a middle tone is balanced, the highlight tones will have a color cast of one color, and the shadow tones will have a cast of the complementary color.

Because the photographic step tablet being used in this procedure is made of a photographic silver image, while the transparencies from which the internegatives are being made have dye images, a print from an internegative that has a perfectly neutral gray scale may not be perfectly balanced for the transparency. This can be corrected by optimizing the internegative filter pack based on typical production transparencies.

Detailed instructions for comparing test curves with a set of reference curves and interpreting differences in terms of correcting filtration and exposure are given in E-24S and E-225T.

Making Color Transparencies from Color Negatives

There are often requirements for color transparencies when the original is an internegative or an original camera negative.

KODAK VERICOLOR Print Film 4111 (ESTAR Thick Base) is made for this purpose. It is available in sheet sizes from 4 x 5 inches up to 20 x 24 inches.

It is designed for exposure times of 10 to 120 seconds and balanced for 3200 K tungsten illumination. It is processed using KODAK FLEXICOLOR Chemicals (Process C-41). (KODAK VERICOLOR Slide Films 5072 and SO-279 are available in 35mm width for making color slides from color negatives and are discussed on page 122.)

Details are given in KODAK Publication No. E-24, *KODAK VERICOLOR Slide and Print Films.*

Except for processing, this film is printed in a manner similar to that for KODAK EKTACOLOR Paper. An approximate starting filter pack for negatives on KODAK Internegative Film would be about 60M + 50Y. Starting packs for other Kodak color negative films are given in the publication mentioned above.

A typical exposure of 10 to 20 seconds is usually about right when the illumination at the printing surface is 2 footcandles. With a white piece of paper on the enlarger easel, 2 footcandles is achieved when a reflection exposure meter reads 1/8 sec at f/6.7 (halfway between f/8 and f/5.6) when the meter is set at a speed of ISO 400.

A visual method of controlling color balance is usually adequate.

Make a test strip, giving a series of exposures such as 5, 7, 10, 14, and 20 seconds. Look at the color balance of the correctly exposed area. If the color balance is off in one direction, add that color filtration to the pack. If for example, the test print is too yellow, add yellow filtration. Judge the test on an illuminator with a color temperature that matches the illuminator on which the transparency will be displayed. To find how much filtration to change, use viewing filters that are complementary to the color cast. If the cast is yellow, use blue viewing filters. Look at the middle tones. When you find how much blue viewing filter is required, add half that amount of yellow to the pack:

Example:

Original color cast	Yellow
Viewing filter that corrects	CC20B
Add to pack	CC10Y

If color paper prints are regularly made with on-easel densitometry, the densitometry can be calibrated for VERICOLOR Print Film, which is likely to have a different balance than EKTACOLOR Paper. The same techniques are used, however.

The upper illustration was made directly from an original color transparency. The lower illustration was made from a two-step duplicate transparency. A color internegative was made of the original. The internegative was printed on KODAK VERICOLOR Print Film to make the duplicate transparency.

Printing from Color Negatives

Starting Filter Packs for Printing KODAK Color Negative Films onto KODAK VERICOLOR Print Film 4111

KODAK Films	Enlargers Using Dichroic Filters with Tungsten-Halogen Lamps
GOLD 100, 200, 400, EKTAR 25 Professional, ROYAL GOLD 25, 100, 200, 400, 1000, EKTAPRESS Plus 100, 200, 400, 1600*, PRO 100, 400, 400MC	20M + 30Y
VERICOLOR III Professional, Type S	20M + 35Y
VERICOLOR II Professional, Type L	20M + 25Y

*For push-processed films, you may need to adjust the filtration.

Note: Filter recommendations are for negatives made on daylight films exposed with daylight or electronic flash illumination, or for tungsten film exposed with tungsten light. Negatives made on daylight film under tungsten light will require more yellow filtration.

As indicated above, the film is processed in KODAK FLEXICOLOR Chemicals (Process C-41). For small-scale production, a tank process can be used. Roller-transport processors are made that process sizes (sheets or rolls) up to about 50 inches in width. Drum-type processors are made to process sheets up to about 16 x 20 inches in size. These produce large-size transparencies for display purposes.

For a small-scale tank process, replenishers can be added manually based on tables. For large-scale production, Process C-41 monitoring strips are generally used to monitor the process. Replenishers are added automatically.

The following publications cover the various aspects of processing with the Process C-41.

No.	Publication Name
E-24	*KODAK VERICOLOR Slide and Print Films*
R-19	*KODAK Color Darkroom DATAGUIDE*
R-25	*KODAK Color Print Viewing Filter Kit*

A Two-Step Color Duplicating Process

The normal method of duplicating transparencies is to use KODAK EKTACHROME Duplicating Film 6121 and use a one-step duplicating procedure. (See page 93.) In cases where the original has delicate highlights, it may be difficult to reproduce these with the one-step process.

A two-step duplication can be used to obtain improved highlight tone reproduction. An internegative is made from the transparency and printed on VERICOLOR Print Film. Properly exposed, the internegative corrects for the compression of highlight tones in the transparency. With two-step duplication, care must be taken at each step to minimize any loss in quality such as a loss of sharpness.

DUPLICATING FADED TRANSPARENCIES
The method of making color internegatives from transparencies on KODAK VERICOLOR Internegative Film can be used to "restore" faded transparencies.

Overall contrast (density range) is increased by increasing the overall exposure. Where one dye layer has faded more than the others, this layer is given additional exposure by changing the filter pack. The internegative can then be used to print a new transparency on KODAK VERICOLOR Print Film. It can also be used to make color prints on one of the KODAK EKTACOLOR Papers.

KODAK VERICOLOR Slide Film 5072 and SO-279
This slide film is a 35mm and long roll film version of VERICOLOR Print Film. The 5072 film is available in long rolls, while the SO-279 film is available in the 135-36 magazine format. It is printed in a similar manner. The film is designed for exposures from 1/4 to 8 seconds with a 3200 K tungsten source.

This film is usually used to make slides from color negatives and internegatives using professional optical printers. It can be used, however, in a 35mm copy setup when the negative is placed in an illuminator and "copied" on the VERICOLOR Slide Film placed in the camera. It is rarely printed with an enlarger or contact-printed. Details are given in KODAK Publication No. E-24, *KODAK VERICOLOR Slide and Print Films.*

KODAK DURATRANS Display Material

This material is essentially a slightly denser color paper emulsion coated on a translucent film base. It is designed to make large display transparencies (color positives).

It is printed from color negatives and internegatives in the same manner as KODAK EKTACOLOR Papers and processed in KODAK EKTACOLOR RA Chemicals for Process RA-4 using a 6-minute developing time.

While small transparencies can be processed in small-drum processors or trays, most professional work is processed in the same roller-transport processors used to process EKTACOLOR Paper. DURATRANS Material is not designed to make transparencies for halftone reproduction. However, it offers a less costly method of making color positives for display.

Making Black-and-White Interpositives and Black-and-White Duplicate Negatives

A black-and-white duplicate negative can be made in one step using KODAK Professional B/W Duplicating Film as described previously. It can also be made in two steps using an intermediate called an interpositive or a diapositive. The reason that you might want to create a duplicate negative in two steps instead of one is that you can exercise more control over the quality of the duplicate negative in two steps than in one. In fact, the amount of control is so great that technicians sometimes make a corrected diapositive and a duplicate negative for printing in preference to printing the original negative. The extra step makes more retouching possible (the diapositive can be enlarged) and eliminates the risk associated with retouching an original negative. There are also more opportunities to manipulate local tone control through dodging, burning-in, intensification, dyeing, and chemical reduction.

The format (size) of the film that you use to make the interpositive and negative depends upon the equipment available and upon the method of printing that is preferred. The best quality is produced by using a large-format film for the interpositive and duplicate negative. If a large-format enlarger is not available to print the negatives, they can be contact-printed. Local treatment (retouching, dyeing, intensification, or reduction) is made easier by the use of a large-format internegative and duplicate negative. Interpositives can be made on KODAK Commercial Film 4127 (ESTAR Base). Contrast can be reduced by moderately overexposing and shortening the developing time.

KODAK Commercial Film is easier to handle in the darkroom. Because it is a blue-sensitive film, it can be handled under safelight conditions normally used only for printing. The interpositive can be exposed with an enlarger or by contact. When exposing with an enlarger the original negative should be oriented in the negative carrier the same as it would be for making a print (emulsion down). The film for the diapositive is held down on an easel covered with black paper. It is inserted emulsion side up. Because film is more sensitive to light than paper, when exposing film under an enlarger, care must be taken to avoid fogging. Light leaks from the enlarger bouncing against a light-colored wall can create a substantial amount of image-degrading fog. Dirty lenses can be a source of flare, which can also degrade the image quality.

When the interpositive is being exposed, dodging and burning-in can be done as if a print were being made. Only dark-colored tools should be used, but dodging tools can be white on top for easier visibility during the exposure.

It is important to make the interpositive with enough exposure so that highlight detail is recorded above the toe of the characteristic curve. This will help preserve highlight tonal separation. The appearance of the interpositive should be darker than a transparency that has good density for viewing. Diffuse highlight density should be at least 0.30.

The duplicate negative is usually contact-printed from the interpositive. This reduces the possibility of flare and sharpness loss due to enlarger optics.

Contact exposures of both the interpositive and the duplicate negative can be made in a contact frame or under a heavy sheet of glass. Black paper should be used as a backing to prevent halation. The original negative is placed emulsion-to-emulsion on top of the unexposed interpositive film or an interpositive is placed emulsion-to-emulsion with the unexposed duplicate negative film. The enlarger light or a small bare bulb can be used to expose the film.

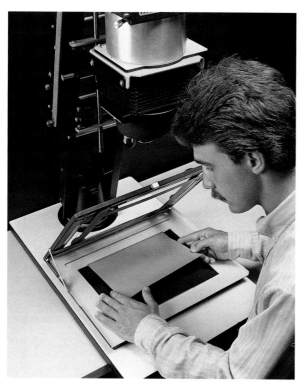

Film is being placed on the easel to make an enlarged interpositive from a black-and-white negative. This is done in the dark when panchromatic film is being used or under a red safelight when the film is orthochromatic.

To do this visually is difficult but not impossible. The experienced printer can tell by looking at a negative whether it is excessively contrasty or extremely flat. The printer can usually tell by observation whether a negative has a density range suitable to print on a paper grade close to normal with a particular enlarger or contact printer. The experienced technician can thus determine if the original negative is high or low in contrast and make the appropriate exposure and development modifications when making the interpositive and duplicate negative. Most of the contrast adjustments are made when making the duplicate negative rather than the interpositive, because visually it is easier to judge contrast when the original is a negative. Negative contrast is reduced by overexposing and underdeveloping. Contrast is increased by slightly underexposing and overdeveloping.

With a densitometer it is possible to make accurate density range measurements. Negatives to be printed on a condenser enlarger with a Grade 2 paper usually require a density range of 0.80 to 0.90. For a more detailed discussion of density range, see Publication F-5, *KODAK Professional Black-and-White Films*. Negatives to be printed on a diffusion enlarger will require a density range of 1.00 to 1.10 with a Grade 2 paper. More often the upper part of these ranges is used rather than the lower part. The negative density range required will vary because of a number of factors that influence the system such as: the brand of photographic paper, the enlarger, the lens, the amount of flare from surfaces in the darkroom, paper developer, and personal preference in print quality. To determine the required negative density range for a particular set of circumstances, choose a negative that prints well on a Grade 2 photographic paper. Read the density of a diffuse highlight (an area that prints just darker than white) and read a shadow tone that prints just lighter than the darkest part of the print. The difference between the shadow and highlight densities is the required negative density range for that enlarger (or contact printer) using the same photographic paper and developer.

The same film that is used to make the interpositive can be used to make the duplicate negative. To make duplicate negatives that have good printing characteristics it is important that the density range of the duplicate negative matches the density range required for the photographic paper and printing system that will be used to print the negative. Because original negatives do not always have a density range that matches the printing system, it is very practical to alter the density range or contrast when making the duplicate so that it is close to the density range required for that particular printing system.

The upper illustration is from a print that was made from the original negative.

The lower illustration is from a print made from a duplicate negative produced by the two-step procedure.

This black-and-white print was made from a black-and-white negative that was made from an original color negative by the two-step duplication process.

Once the required negative density range is determined, the density range of duplicate negatives can be aimed at this range. To do this, first measure the density range of the original negative. If the density range is longer (indicating higher contrast), then the duplicate negative should be overexposed and underdeveloped. The amount of overexposure and underdevelopment for a given density change must be determined by trial and error. Keep records of the amounts of density changes that occur with different development times for future reference.

The interpositive is usually made so that it reproduces the density range of the original negative, and contrast changes are usually made when the duplicate negative is made. However, if the difference between the original negative density range and the required density range is large (0.40 or more), the contrast can be reduced in the interpositive step also, so that development times remain of reasonable length.

To increase the contrast of a low-contrast original, slight underexposure and longer development times are required. Again, contrast is usually increased in the last step, but if the density range of the original is a great deal lower than the required negative density range, the contrast can be increased in both the interpositive and the duplicate negative.

Making Black-and-White Negatives from Color Negatives

A black-and-white negative can be made from a color negative in much the same way as a black-and-white negative is duplicated in two steps. The significant difference is the choice of films and developers.

Interpositives can be made on several KODAK Films—EKTAPAN Film 4162, PLUS-X Pan Professional Film 4147, T-MAX 100 Professional Film 4052, or other general-purpose medium-contrast films. The film/developer combination should produce an interpositive that is close in density range to the final negative and slightly dark for viewing. The film/developer combination will need to be higher contrast than would be used for black-and-white duplicate negatives because black-and-white negative films generally yield low contrast when exposed to color negatives. The density range of the final negative should match the required density range for the printing system being used.

The black-and-white negative can be made on either KODAK Commercial Film 4127 or KODAK Technical Pan Film 2415.

126

Making Title Slides

Attractive title slides can be made fast and easily with a minimum of equipment employing basic copying techniques. Using a basic copy setup with a 35mm camera, black-and-white artwork can be photographed to make the slides with either white letters on a colored background or colored letters on a black background. Other, more sophisticated techniques are also available for making title slides but are beyond the scope of this book.

Black-and-white artwork that is to be used for title slides can be made by using typeset copy, by applying press-type to clean white paper or board, or by using type from a typewriter with a carbon ribbon. If many title slides are to be made, it is convenient to have all the artwork made to the same size so that copying can be done at the same magnification and focus. See the upper left illustration on page 28 for an appropriate copying setup.

Usually it is necessary to have a macro lens or other close-focusing method for the camera when the characters in the original copy are small. Otherwise the characters in the title slides will be hard to read when projected. Typewritten characters on a 3 x 5-inch card produce about the smallest text on a slide that can be easily read when the slide is projected.

Colored Letters/Black Background: To make slides with a black background and colored or clear letters, the artwork is photographed with a high-contrast black-and-white film such as KODALITH Ortho Film 6556, Type 3. This film is available for 35mm in 100-ft. rolls. It can be loaded into 135-size magazines with a bulk film loader using KODAK SNAP-CAP 135 Magazines. It is also available in 135-36 magazines under the name of KODAK EKTAGRAPHIC HC Slide Film.

KODALITH Ortho Film has an exposure index of 8. Light meter readings should be made with a *KODAK Gray Card* instead of the copy because the large white areas of the copy will cause the light meter to indicate less exposure than is necessary. KODALITH Ortho Film can be processed in KODALITH Developer with a light red safelight (KODAK 1A Safelight Filter).

KODAK Technical Pan Film 2415 can also be used for this purpose. KODAK Technical Pan Film is available in 135-36 exposure magazines and in 35mm 150-foot rolls. For this application, KODAK Technical Pan Film should be exposed at EI 200 and developed in KODAK DEKTOL Developer for 3 minutes at 68°F (20°C) with agitation at 30-second intervals.

The processed films can be mounted and used as slides without adding color. They also can be dyed or sandwiched with filters to add color to the clear letters. Dyeing can be done by immersing the processed film in a liquid dye such as food coloring or transparent watercolors. Felt-tip markers that are fresh can also be used to add color to the slides.

A title slide made on an extremely high-contrast black-and-white film such as one of the KODALITH Films or KODAK Technical Pan Film developed for 3 minutes in KODAK DEKTOL Developer 1:2. The slide was placed in a yellow dye and rinsed before drying.

After the films are dried, imperfections can be retouched by applying opaque to slides made on KODALITH Film. Imperfections such as dirt, cut lines, or pinholes appear as clear white marks on the film. These marks are easily eliminated by painting them with KODAK Opaque (Black or Red) or by using a technical pen with black ink to cover them.

Clear Letters/Colored Background: A very attractive type of title slide can be created that has a bright, vivid background color with clear letters. The same-type original can be used for this technique: black letters with a white background. The only requirement that is different is that the originals must be clean and free of cut marks. Cut marks are the dark lines that are created when one piece of paper is pasted on top of another. They are common on "paste-up" artwork. Because the background will be photographed as a colored tone, there is no opportunity to opaque or retouch the marks.

If the original is a paste-up, copy it on a high-contrast film as just described. Opaque the cut lines and make a black-and-white print from the opaqued negative. This copy print can be used as an original for the next step.

To make the slides, the artwork is photographed on a film such as KODAK VERICOLOR Slide Film 5072 or SO-279. These films are normally used for making slides from color negatives. KODAK VERICOLOR Slide Film 5072 is available in long rolls (35mm x 100 feet). KODAK VERICOLOR Slide Film SO-279 is a similar film that is available in 35mm 36-exposure magazines. Both of these films are processed in KODAK FLEXICOLOR Chemicals (Process C-41).

The exposure index for VERICOLOR Slide Film 5072 and SO-279 is 8.

The colors are produced by using filters over the lens while copying the artwork. Because the film is a negative/positive film, a filter approximating the complement of the desired color must be used. Normally the film is used to make slides from color negatives that have an orange mask. As a result, the film will produce a dark red color if no filter at all is used. The table below lists some of the colors that are possible and the corresponding KODAK WRATTEN Filters that produce the colors. The table is based upon the use of a 3200 K tungsten light source. Exposure times should be kept between 1/10 and 8 seconds for best results.

Background Color	KODAK WRATTEN Gelatin Filters	Exposure Increase (in stops)
Diazo Blue	12 or 15 (yellow) + 85B or 86 (orange)	+2
Cyan	29 (red)	+4
Green	34A (deep magenta)	+4
Red	38 (light blue)	+4
Orange	44 (cyan)	+4
Yellow	45 (deep blue-green)	+4
Magenta	61 (deep green)	+5
Yellow-Brown	47 (deep blue)	+4
Dark Red	No Filter	—

Colors may also be created by making the artwork with black letters on colored paper. This, however, reduces the flexibility to change colors if the color that is produced is not satisfactory.

A reverse-text title slide made by copying a black-and-white original through a light blue filter (see table) on KODAK VERICOLOR Slide Film 5072 and processed as a color negative in Process C-41 with KODAK FLEXICOLOR Chemicals.

A black-and-white negative like the slide on the left was contact-printed on KODALITH Film to make a title of black letters on a transparent background. This was placed in a raised position over a piece of artwork far enough below the title to be out of focus when copied. It was then copied through a yellow filter and processed as a color negative.

BLACK-AND-WHITE SLIDES

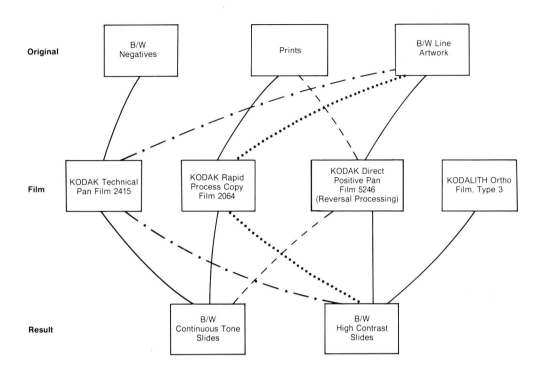

COLOR SLIDES

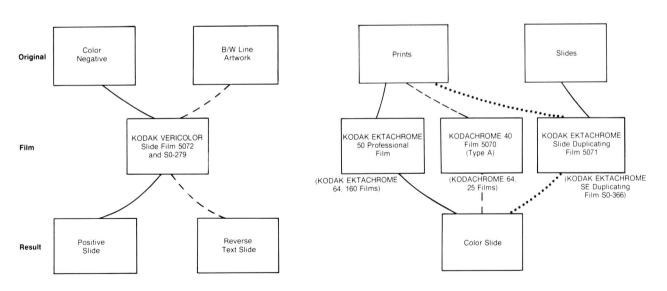

The schematic drawings on this page show a number of methods for making slides from a variety of originals using different films. All of the films shown are available in 35 mm format and can be used to make slides either by copying or duplicating.

ELECTRONIC METHODS
OF COPYING AND DUPLICATING

The KODAK Pro Photo CD imaging workstation is used by photographic labs and service bureaus. Images produced on 35mm, 70mm, 120/220, and 4 x 5 film formats are copied onto photo CD master discs. Once an image is digitized, it can be viewed, retouched, and manipulated using image-enhancement software, then saved as a digital file or output.

The recent growth in electronic forms of photography has produced a number of important options in duplication and copy methods. The best of these are based on the use of digital recordings (as opposed to still video recordings), and some of these approaches have begun to displace traditional chemical-based copy and duplication procedures in service laboratories and photography studios. The reason for this is that digital recordings offer a much higher degree of control over the reproduction of the original with many more options to alter the image, especially in the case of correcting contrast, brightness, and color as well as in retouching and restoration.

In general, the high-end digital equipment for carrying out these procedures for all forms of photographic images and for making accurate copies is very expensive and, until recently, was usually found only in service bureaus and larger photographic laboratories. So-called desktop systems, based on powerful personal computers, have, however, become available in recent years from a wide range of manufacturers. These smaller, comparatively less-expensive systems are now showing up more and more in larger photographic studios, a wide range of service laboratories, and in other areas where photography plays a dominant role, such as in graphic design studios. Most observers see a continued increase in the use of these desktop systems as electronic imaging in general becomes more cost-effective for the end user.

Since digital methods are based on complex electronic equipment and elaborate software programs, one chapter can only introduce these methods. Furthermore, since most photographers who become personally involved with this form of photography will do so with desktop systems, the emphasis in this introductory chapter will be on those approaches as opposed to the larger equipment found in service bureaus and labs. Thus, the general goals in this chapter will be to explain the digital recording process, give an overview of the equipment and software involved in digital copying and duplication, and, along the way, to make note of the extraordinary capabilities of digital copy and duplication techniques.

The Digital Photography System

The differences between a silver halide and digital image begin at the moment the picture is taken, or "captured" as it is called in digital parlance. In traditional photography, clicking the shutter introduces light that causes an initial chemical reaction on the film which is later completed in the chemical processing of that film. The pictorial outcome is the result of layers of chemical reactions among molecules which are forming new compounds. The end product is a picture made up of chains of these compounds that gives the illusion of a continuous-tone, seamless image.

In a digital capture, the light is recorded electronically by the activation of millions of tiny recording points across a surface referred to as a Charge-Coupled Device or CCD. Each of these points is eventually represented through the binary language of the computer as a single pixel or picture element on the computer screen. Each pixel can then be separately controlled in the computer with powerful software programs which take these millions of bits of binary information originally generated when the light hit the CCD surface and literally reconstruct the original scene, pixel by pixel. Thus, a digital image is not unlike a film image in that it is made up of infinitely small parts that are perceived as a whole. But unlike film, each of these millions of parts can be individually controlled, and that, as we will see shortly, is the basis of digital photography's advantage over film in general and when it is used in the duplication and copy processes.

Probably the most important consideration that permeates the entire digital loop is the question of image quality, and that is largely determined by the density of the data coming from the original recording. As a broad generalization, the higher the number of pixels across the CCD, the more data per area of the original is recorded and therefore, the greater the potential for a higher quality image. The common means of expressing this is to list the number of pixels horizontally x vertically. For example, one of the newest digital cameras in the KODAK Professional DCS Camera line that is jointly manufactured with Canon U.S.A., Inc., the KODAK Professional EOS•DCS 5 Digital Camera, has a pixel rating of 1,524 x 1,012 for a total of 1.5 million pixels.

The KODAK Professional EOS•DCS 5 Digital Camera is an autofocus SLR digital still camera based on the Canon EOS-1N and designed for rapid turnaround of high-quality images. It is compatible with the Canon EF lenses and most EOS accessories. The camera pictured is the KODAK Professional EOS•DCS 5c Digital Camera which offers 36-bit full-color capture. Black-and-white and infrared models are also available.

The Leaf DCB II is a high-end digital camera back that attaches to most medium and large format cameras. It makes separate red, green, and blue exposures requiring three passes of the linear array and has an ISO equivalent of 25 for color (200 for B&W). While problematic for some applications, these features are generally not drawbacks for copying and duplicating.

While it is tempting to compare pixel ratings to film ratings of granularity, lines of resolution, or film response curves, in a practical sense, such attempts at direct comparisons do not work very well. There are, indeed, many pitfalls in trying to compare an electronic image directly to a photochemical one. For one thing, recent developments in the way some software programs process basic information from the CCD source are now introducing new paradigms in order to construct the image. For example, in the case of the Leaf Systems CatchLight digital recording back, that company has combined an advanced processing paradigm with new pixel configurations on the CCD. This supposedly produces a recording potential of light that is "closer to the way humans actually see." Consequently, purely electronic concepts such as "extrapolation," "fuzzy logic," "data compression," and other so-called system approaches to the evaluation and use of binary data will affect the quality of the final image in various ways. In some cases, combinations of some of these methods even provide the means to extend basic CCD recorded data in the production of digital images so that a better image is possible. What this boils down to is that just considering total pixels as the primary indicator of quality when looking at the specifications of a particular capture device may come to represent more of a "potential" for high quality as more and more progress is made in the way the software processes the binary information.

Image Acquisition

The first step in the use of digital imaging techniques is to enter the visual information about the subject into the computer. At the moment, two options are available to photographers; either they can photograph the subject with a digital camera or convert a traditional image, as in a print or transparency, into a digital image through the use of a scanner. Each, as we will see, represents an approach with distinct advantages and disadvantages. Nevertheless, the technology used in both approaches is similar in that it is based on a CCD surface responding to the light being focused on its surface. The advantage of digital cameras is that there is no need to first shoot and develop the film and then scan the results into the computer. Also, there is the added expense of having to either buy the scanner or pay for each scan. On the other hand, the cost of the higher-end digital cameras is quite substantial and requires an initial investment that probably needs to be justified by a high volume of work.

DIGITAL CAMERA CAPTURE
Images can be recorded by digital cameras (or digital camera backs) equipped with CCD surfaces in one of two basic ways. In one method, CCD surfaces are configured as a single block chip, usually in a rectangular shape, which reacts to the focused light from a conventional lens for a "full capture" of the subject. In this configuration, the CCD surface is essentially taking the place of film while most all other functions of the camera, from motor drive to autofocus, remain the same. Good examples of this are the KODAK DCS Cameras which use either Nikon or Canon bodies fitted with Kodak's proprietary CCD chips as part of a back that takes the place of film.

Similarly, the use of a digital back leaves most of the camera's basic functions intact. Again, the CCD-equipped electronic back basically takes the place of the film and records the light in a digital mode.

At the present time, most camera back designs tend to be more "studio-oriented" units partly because many are used on sophisticated view cameras, such as the Sinar line, and partly because it makes operational sense to hook in directly to a computer. On the other hand, some of the KODAK DCS Digital Camera models based on Nikon and Canon bodies are designed to be used outdoors or on location, as in a museum or art gallery.

One of the main determinations of how mobile a digital camera or digital camera back arrangement can be is the way data is handled once the CCD is activated by the light. Thus, capture data can be "dumped" directly into the computer via a direct cable link from camera to computer as would be practical in a studio or somewhat less so on location with the use of a laptop/portable computer. A second approach is to use some sort of in-camera storage media to record the pictures. This stored information can be downloaded later into a computer. What is even more desirable is to have an in-camera storage media such as a disk or card that can be removed from the camera for the downloading procedure.

Lately, one method of in-camera storage has been to use PCMCIA technology. These small removable cards, which have become commonplace with users of portable laptop computers, are now capable of high data density storage in the 100-plus megabyte range. The KODAK Professional EOS•DCS 5 Digital Camera mentioned earlier, for example, uses removable PCMCIA storage cards. This gives the user the ability to shoot and store several pictures depending on how much data is being captured by the CCD in each exposure. Once the data is recorded, the card is removed from the camera and downloaded into a computer equipped with a PCMCIA slot. The interchangeable nature of these cards also gives the user the option to shoot more total exposures per session since one needs only to replace them with empty cards as needed.

Besides using a single CCD chip surface to make a full capture of the subject with a digital camera or camera back, there is a second recording approach that relies on a scanning action. Here, instead of having all the focused light from a lens fall on the recording points of a single CCD chip, the pixels are arranged in a thin line across a bar that covers the entire vertical area of the field to be recorded. The exposure is then made by having the bar move steadily in a horizontal direction across the field of focused light from the lens in what is referred to as a "linear scan." A similar mechanism is used in digital scanners intended to convert photographs (flatbed scanners) and film (film scanners) to digital data.

One of the most important operational advantages of a scan arrangement is that large areas can be covered with just a thin line of pixels on the CCD. Obviously, the subject must be static and not move at all during the scanning period, which is invariably the situation in copy and duplication work.

In addition to "full capture" and "linear scan"-type recordings, there are two methods which are used by both of these approaches to gather up all the chromatic information. Either the color information is all recorded in one CCD exposure (one-pass), which is also all that is necessary for a monochrome original, or in three separate RGB or red, green, and blue exposures (three-pass). Only a very small number of scanners are designed to directly output CMYK data. In a one-pass arrangement, the various CCD recording points have been divided up and separately sensitized to either red, green, or blue and react to these various colors in the light coming from the subject. Thus, all chromatic data is collected at once. When the color data from this pass reaches the computer, the software then "mixes" these primaries in proportion to their occurrence in the original light of the recording to obtain all other colors. CMYK conversions for the purposes of print publications can then be made later using photo management programs such as Photoshop.

In the three-pass approach, each exposure is limited to either red, green, or blue. This means that, unlike the single-pass approach, all of the recording points are being used in each pass to gather chromatic data in just the color set for that pass, rather than dividing up the points to just be sensitive to one color. In theory, this should also result in a higher-quality recording, because all of the recording points are being used in each pass as opposed to dividing them up according to color sensitivity.

Sinar P2 with KODAK Professional DCS 465 Digital Camera Back

Because the materials used to construct light-sensitive chips become exponentially more expensive to produce as the size of the chip increases, recording devices that use the linear scan method will require a smaller number of recording points and will be less expensive to produce than the larger chips used in the full capture-type cameras and backs. For this reason, it is possible to build a linear array scanner made up of just a single line of CCD structures at a reasonable cost, as in certain lower-priced flatbed scanners.

As with the single-pass recording, the computer takes all the color data and mixes it to produce the full color palette of the original according to the proportions of each color present for each recording point. Once again, all this is made possible because in a digital recording, the computer software can control all aspects of the image by working with each individual pixel.

The use of a digital camera or digital camera back to capture images for the computer represents a complete digital system as, for example, when the image is recorded with a digital camera on a copy stand. Typical examples would include using either a digital camera or a digital camera back, such as the KODAK Professional DCS 465 Digital Camera Back on a medium or large format studio camera. While there are advantages to this approach, as will be pointed out below, this is the most expensive way of entering the digital loop since these cameras and backs are quite costly, ranging from approximately $8,000—$25,000.

In addition, there are some operational considerations that may influence the decision as to whether or not to use this form of digital capture, as when deciding how to go about copying an original piece of artwork, whether on a copy stand or as it hangs on a wall. The major consideration here is the high levels of light (and therefore heat) that are necessary to produce reasonable recording levels when working with many digital cameras. Work with conventional cameras and film typically means shooting with strobe for larger subjects and quartz/tungsten light on copy stands, the latter of which can be turned off or reduced except when the actual exposure is made. This, as we will explain shortly, cannot be easily done with the continuous light used in digital recordings. The illumination requirements for many digital cameras call for powerful, continuous, "flicker-free" light sources.

The reason for this is that all scan-type recordings in the presently available technology require an even, unchanging, and very bright light source that has to remain on during the entire exposure. This applies equally to one-pass or three-pass scan-type digital recordings. Otherwise, parts of the recording will show uneven levels of exposure and/or color shifts which invariably occur when continuous-light sources "flicker." Such flicker can come from line voltage changes (producing color wavelength changes) or because some characteristic of the light unit itself alters the color characteristics of the light output slightly. Obviously, then, working with any kind of scanning digital capture requires a much more critical light source.

When single-digital-chip cameras are used to capture all the light reflected off the subject in a single pass, a strobe light source can be used. But when a single-chip camera is used in a three-pass capture, there is a need to have exactly the same level and quality of light in all three of the exposures. While high-quality, reliable strobes can be used here, some photographers prefer to use the same voltage-stabilized, continuous-light sources used with scan backs to guarantee three separate accurate color recordings with single-chip cameras.

Currently, the preferred flicker-free continuous-illumination source is HMI-generated light, which are large, heavy lights often used in the movies that draw high levels of power. Obviously, there are many types of original art, from paintings to photographs, that may be damaged as a result of these conditions. For that reason, it might be better to consider using the hybrid approach and photographing the original on conventional films first. Furthermore, the power requirements of these lights are significantly more than other continuous sources such as tungsten bulb and quartz. Finally, the size and weight of these lights will increase the need for assistants and larger-capacity transportation.

Another operational consideration comes from the generalization that the best image quality has been from digital cameras using the three-pass, scan-type configuration. Today, this means basically working with either a medium or large format camera and a digital back to obtain the largest files in the recording. This is because, given the present technology, these camera backs have much larger recording areas. For example, in the case of the Dicomed Digital Back intended for use on view cameras, the CCD linear array roughly scans over the field of view of a 4 x 5-inch format. By contrast, a single-pass, rectangular-chip camera back usually has a total recording surface less than the size of a 35mm frame.

The use of a high-quality digital camera by a photographer who has to copy three-dimensional objects or flat art on location, as in a museum or gallery, has some very real advantages over conventional cameras. For example, photographing something like a large, highly reflective painting which needs to be illuminated evenly can be done in a very accurate way by viewing the captured object on the screen of a portable computer. Thus, using such software programs as Photoshop or Live Picture, the photographer can analyze the results by using mathematical paradigms that supply specific data about color, brightness, contrast, etc. This allows the photographer to see exactly what is being recorded and provides more image information than conventional photography setups, even those that include the use of instant-film checks.

Dicomed's BigShot CCD Back uses a 6 x 6 cm CCD linear array to capture images at a resolution of 4096 x 4096 pixels.

Under these recording conditions, preliminary adjustments in contrast and brightness in the recording itself or in the lighting being used to take the picture can be made on location based on what the computer image indicates. This is accomplished by examining the various ways the software represents the data as in histograms, curves, scattergrams, and other quick-reference displays. The software gives the photographer the means to shift and change these distributions in general and specific ways to produce literally any degree of alteration.

Besides the ability to analyze the physical characteristics of an image, digital recordings offer the photographer several other advantages. For example, once the photographer begins to use digitized images in the computer, it is just a logical next step, for example, to work directly with the publication layout for which the image is intended. This means that the photographer can make cropping decisions "on the spot" that will fit exactly into the layout or anticipate problems with matching the captured image with the layout requirements which may not be obvious until arrival on location.

A flicker-free, continuous light source is preferred for digital photography. HMI (high-intensity metal vapor discharge lamp) lighting, such as the Sinar Broncolor HMI 575, offers three times more light per watt than quartz halogen lamps.

Hybrid Digital Capture

The second form of capture has been called "hybrid digital photography" because instead of using a digital camera for the capture, the subject is photographed using conventional photographic methods and then digitized in order to be placed into the computer. The original print or transparency is then scanned into the computer through the use of either a flatbed or film scanner. The difference between the two devices is that the linear scan CCD surface of a flatbed scanner measures the intensity and quality of reflected light coming off the print's surface, while a film scanner does the same for the light coming through the transparency or negative. Actually, there is little difference in the recording technology between digital cameras and scanners since both approaches are using CCD structures to produce the image. So, the generalizations that have been made about one- and three-pass for digital cameras apply to these devices, and, as with digital cameras, the better scanners are capable of producing larger files.

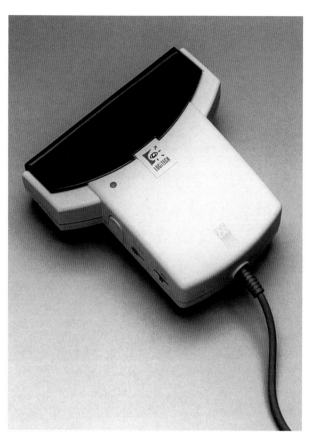

Scanners are essentially used to make digital copies of conventional photographs. Pricing varies widely and is largely dependent on the desired quality of the resulting scan. This Logitech EasyTouch is a gray-scale hand scanner with a maximum resolution of 400 dpi.

This is to say nothing of unanticipated problems with lighting the subject or overcoming photographic complications produced by the location itself, such as would come from uncontrollable and interfering light sources. Again, with the layout in the computer and the ability to "drop in" a captured image on the spot, some problems do not have to wait for a meeting with the publisher or art director to be dealt with.

In addition to all these considerations, there are any number of other ways that the photographer can influence or even control the outcome of the final image by virtue of the fact that the image is digitized and in the computer. This will depend, to a large degree, on what role the photographer is playing in the total production, of which capturing the original image is only a part. For example, adjusting an image to a specific color balance or ink density for the printer in the separations is something that a digitally knowledgeable photographer can carry out on the computer. All of this, of course, raises a larger issue beyond the scope of this chapter, and that is, how digital photography per se is going to change the traditional role of photographers specializing in copy and duplication work.

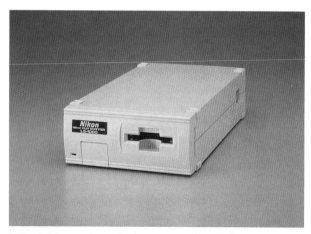

Nikon's LS-1000 SuperCoolscan can produce full-color 2,700 dpi scans from 35mm slides or negatives.

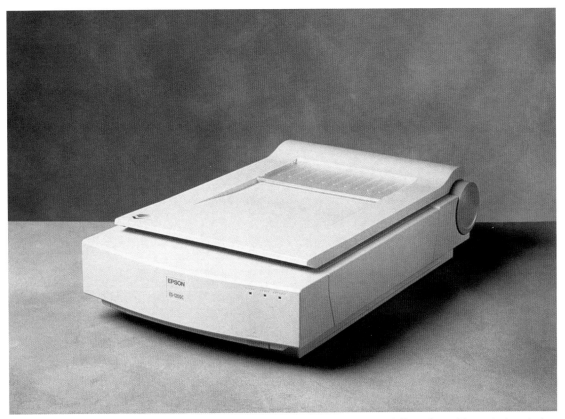

Epson's ES-1200C-Pro is a 30-bit flatbed scanner that can recognize over one billion different hues. The optical resolution is 600 dpi and using software, it has an interpolated resolution of up to 4800 dpi.

Since the total number of pixels used in a chip camera or camera back is likely to be greater than the number of pixels in the thin line of a linear scanner, the best way to think about the quality of the capture is not by comparing pixels but by the file size of the capture as measured in megabytes. As pointed out earlier, file size is not an absolute measure of quality but rather more of an indicator. There is no absolute and directly comparable index or set of numbers that can be used in practical, everyday situations to translate file size to quality. This is because, as has been mentioned, increasingly there are other variables, such as the way a particular software treats the data, which will influence the quality of the final image.

Still, the closest unit of measurement, besides quoting pixel density and the specific type of recording (large surface scans versus single capture, one-pass versus three-pass, etc.), is the file size of the capture. Literally, this is how many bytes of information have actually been captured and stored on some sort of media for use in the computer. Consequently, photographers, photographic lab, and service bureau personnel will often talk of "file sizes" such as a 16MB file, a 64MB file, or ones rated in the 100MB-plus range.

The more binary information as expressed in megabytes captured on the file, the higher the potential for quality. But remember, this also means the need for more powerful computers to move around and change these large numbers of total pixels that make up such high-density files, as well as a storage media that is capable of holding high-density information. So the lesson here is that any increase in the size of the file during capture will have to be matched by a capability of the computer and whatever storage mechanism is used to handle these files.

Digital photography is literally changing by the month and by the type of equipment available. Other considerations such as costs have the potential to change the specific choices available to the photographer. Such changes are far beyond what used to happen when Kodak updated a dupe film or introduced a new copy emulsion. Obviously, the decision as to which of the many approaches to take will be highly dependent on a number of considerations, not the least of which is the quality of the recordings being offered by presently available technology.

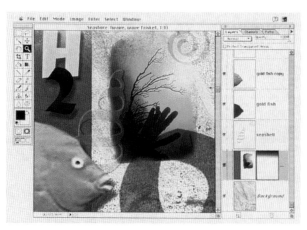

Digital copies of an image can be cropped, color corrected, combined with other images, and otherwise altered with powerful image manipulation software, such as Adobe Photoshop. ©Adobe Systems

Image Management and Manipulation

Once the recording data has been entered into the computer, either directly from a digital camera or scanner, there are many software programs available which deal with the now all-electronic image. In terms of desktop systems, one of the most popular in the U.S. is Adobe Photoshop. Others include Live Picture, Aldus Photostyler, Fractal Design, and Micrografx Picture Publisher, to name just a cross section of examples. Initially, photo management programs were geared to the Apple Macintosh Computer platforms, but the move to have a wide selection on the PC platform in desktop systems is now largely in place. Thus, in terms of desktop computer platforms, the digital imaging market typically available to individual photographers is basically divided between Macintosh and IBM PC compatibles.

Generally, PC computers have cost less (in some cases, significantly less) than Macintosh Computer platforms. In general, however, the cost of both types of computers is now becoming quite reasonable, especially when you consider the prices of top-of-the-line computers just a couple of years ago. The cost of the computer itself, however, represents only part of the investment in digital imaging, since one must add the price of such essential items as large amounts of volatile memory to the basic computer platform. Then there are helpful and even necessary additions in the form of accessory cards and other "plug-ins" that significantly increase the computer's ability to deal with the enormous binary data that makes up a photograph.

Initially, Macintosh Computers and their programs dominated this area because of their unique icon-oriented, initiative-driven software, which non-technical users found quite user-friendly. This was opposed to DOS-based programs with their reliance on coded,

keystroke operations which were anything but intuitive. But with the surge of the icon-based Windows environment as a graphic interface for DOS-operated computers, the situation has been changing. The appearance and operation of the various software programs in both Windows/PC and Macintosh Computer environments have basically altered the situation—there is an increasing use of PC platforms and software. There is also the undeniable trend to have both platforms capable of running each other's software.

Besides the manner in which various software programs operate, the major consideration when working on the computer is speed of operation. Since so much binary data has to be moved around to construct a detailed photograph and then to change it, the computer must have the capability of dealing with enormous files of data very quickly. Otherwise, the operator will execute a command and then have to wait long periods of time while the computer processes the data to carry out the operation. While even the best of today's computers are still unable to carry out all commands in "real time" (virtually instantaneous execution and completion of a command), they have become fast enough to make working at the computer much less time-consuming in terms of waiting for a command to be carried out.

This question of speed of operation, which is such an important point during the computer stage, is based on a number of influential factors, such as (1) the amount of data coming from the capture (file size), (2) the type of CPU on which the particular computer platform is based, (3) the size of the computer's RAM or random access memory, (4) the size of the computer's idle hard drive memories, and other factors such as the use of accelerator boards. In short, the actual speed at which a computer will carry out a command can be influenced by a number of factors. This reality and the tendency of computer technology to change so rapidly should convince any potential buyer of the need to seek the guidance of someone well-versed not only in computer technology, but specifically in the requirements for photographic capture and manipulation as well as output.

The danger here is that the user will purchase a computer that seems to fit his or her immediate needs, but in doing so, fails to consider such questions as (1) how are files to be stored, (2) what are the options to expand the abilities of the computer to handle expanded tasks, (3) how does the system handle multi-tasking (the execution of more than one major function at the same time), and other operational considerations that photographers do not typically know unless they have become familiar with the latest in computer technology and have some idea where the technology will go next.

These are but a few of the basic and critical questions that must be addressed in order to make a reasonable decision about hardware requirements. A good strategy is to take the time to observe any existing setups that are functioning close to your particular goals and to become familiar with different software packages that are on the market. In larger operations, as in institutions or corporations, the use of a professional consultant or agency thoroughly familiar with your particular area is a highly recommended approach.

HOW IMAGE MANAGEMENT SOFTWARE PROGRAMS WORK

There are usually two levels to the software used in digital imaging. The first runs the capture device and the second level involves the management of the image once it has been captured and placed in the computer. The software used by digital scanners and cameras is usually limited in its ability to affect the final image. The purpose of this type of software is to produce as accurate a transfer of the image as possible from the recording device to the computer. Thus, there are limited provisions for management of color, contrast, etc.

For more extensive and specific changes in the image, more powerful image management software such as Photoshop and Live Picture must be used. For this reason, the system requirements in the computer for the capture portion are usually lower than when using the more powerful image management programs. In other words, a fairly low-powered computer with limited RAM space can be used quite nicely to run the capture software, but will take intolerably long to move this data around while using a program like Photoshop.

MAKING LARGER CHANGES IN THE IMAGE

Basically, photo management software programs in the class with Photoshop and Live Picture provide the user with tools with which to affect minor or major changes in the captured image. These tools will vary to some extent within each program but all are geared to allow the user to alter the image in one of two general ways, (1) either by affecting the entire image, as in an overall change in color balance, color saturation, brightness, sharpness, or (2) by changing the content of the image in some very specific way, as in adding or removing parts of the picture.

Most commonly, the larger changes are carried out by calling up various mathematical representations of specific characteristics, as in color distribution in histograms, curves, and other plotted values. Then the users can effectively change the picture by altering these mathematical representations through shifting values on a chart or bending curves to rearrange values, all of which are then carried out by changing the software on command.

Compared to conventional methods of copying or duplication, digital methods have unparalleled capabilities to affect the image by literally changing any of the basic chromatic and exposure characteristics. In other words, not only does the software provide the photographer with an accurate and complete representation of all the key physical elements in a picture but also the means by which to make a full range of changes. And this is to say nothing of how actual visual elements, such as picture content from the details of someone's face to the structure of a diagram, can also be changed. Furthermore, these alterations can be carried out in many variations in order to see and evaluate certain interpretations relatively quickly. In many cases, this evaluation can be done on the computer screen and a decision made without the need to produce any sort of "work print."

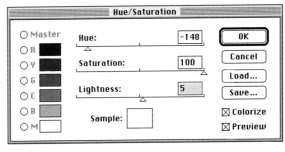

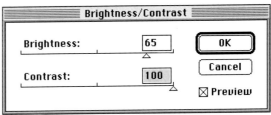

Two examples of dialog boxes for Adobe Photoshop commands.

139

In practical terms, such powerful software programs virtually eliminate all of the traditional problems associated with using conventional films and papers to copy and duplicate subjects. Furthermore, they have the capability to deliver very accurate representations of the subject or any variation desired in minimal time, while maintaining image quality and without having to reshoot.

Finally, duplications of the final image can be made in virtually limitless generations without any loss of quality in any aspect of the visual appearance of the original. Essentially, the conditions of contrast buildup, color shifts, and other well-known problems with film-to-film duplication are eliminated in a digital duplication system.

MAKING SMALLER, SPECIFIC CHANGES IN THE IMAGE

For the second major category of changes that can be done in the computer, namely, specific additions and subtractions in smaller areas, software programs rely heavily on specialized tools to single out and work with parts of the picture. In most cases, these are selected from a display panel or menu which shows them in icon form. The selection of these tools can be made by keystrokes but most often by the use of a mouse or some sort of stylus tool that resembles a pencil. Electronic styluses are used on palettes that pick up their movement and, in some cases, even differences in pressure.

Some of the most useful software tools are referred to as "paint tools," because they can "paint" by adding or removing segments of the picture. Some common examples include paintbrushes, air brushes or spray paint, paint sponges, erasers, smudging tools, cloning tools, and edge-softening tools. By just

Palettes for Adobe Photoshop's paintbrush tool illustrate just a fraction of the control options offered by the program.

taking the literal meaning of these tools, you can get some idea of the ways in which particular parts of a subject can be changed by adding or subtracting elements in a picture.

Each of these tools generally has a wide range of choices as to size of the application and specificity of how the tool actually works. This is analogous to how a different-size brush gives a different amount of coverage or what happens when different amounts of paint are placed on it. This is provided by choices from a second tablet of selections that will, for example, control, as the icon is moved about on the computer screen, how much an eraser will erase, the area a paintbrush will brush, or what color a paintbrush will spread over an area as selected from a palette, which is capable of providing virtually endless hues.

Other selections from other panels will control the type of edge (soft, sharp, feathered, etc.) of the tool's effect. Each program will also have something unique in the way tools function or in the way a standard tool is controlled. These are the differences users come to like and prefer on one program over another or with one tool over another. Also, more than one tool can accomplish a given task, and users often develop favorite combinations as they work with an image. This is often the case when working on more complex changes.

Some of the tools being provided by various computer software programs are especially unique and represent examples of how this technology has changed not only photography in general, but copy and duplication capabilities as well. A particularly good example is what is generally referred to as a cloning tool. Basically, this tool has two functions. First, the user activates its clone function (usually with the click of the mouse), causing it to pick up pixel information from any part of the picture on which it has been placed. Next, the tool is positioned on an area and activated with a different click of the mouse or pressure from a stylus. This results in the simultaneous erasure of what is there and the application of what was cloned. In this way, a dust spot or scratch can be very easily removed and replaced with the identical background that was blocked by its presence using image material directly adjacent to the dust spot. Thus, the removal of dust, scratches, and other flaws can be carried out in minutes, and larger damage, such as tears, can be repaired with just a little more effort.

Another set of tools called "selection tools" are also available in photo management programs and have as their main function the sectioning and "capture" of significant portions of the scene through outlining that structure. For example, tools such as a lasso, magic wand, or pointer can be used to segregate a vase on a table so it can be removed from the picture and then, if desired, placed into another picture in another file.

Still other useful tools classified as "filters" by many programs are capable of changing a whole image (or any captured section of an image) in terms of certain preprogrammed effects from solarization to various types of softening, as well as actually sharpening the lines of the picture.

Perhaps the best analogy that can be made as to the function of tools in photo management programs is that they allow control over the image much like an artist has over a painting, but without having to spend years learning how to control the brush strokes, as well as other mechanical skills associated with the study of using artist's materials. Instead, the computer gives the user control.

Data Storage

One of the realities of modern digital systems is the variety of operating technologies and products that are available in each stage of the digital loop. The different computer platforms and types of software have already been noted, and the situation with data storage is similar. Basically, there are three reasons to store data outside the computer; first, as with film, to be able to use the image again at some later date; second, to be able to transport files to a service bureau or lab so that they can produce hard copies such as prints or transparencies; and third, because leaving files stored on the computer's hard drive will eventually take up too much space and interfere with the ability of the computer to carry out its operations.

To some degree, the size of individual files as well as the number of images will affect the choice in the hardware used for data storage. Here again, the advice of a consultant would be of great help in determining the best choice. The overall problem in this area, however, is that there is no "universal" storage medium which is used by all segments of the digital loop as there is, for example, with the use of standardized 35mm film cassettes in conventional photography.

At the moment, there are several choices, but there appears to be great interest in one particular approach developed by Kodak, called KODAK Photo CD. Other approaches which include various forms of magnetic tape storage, such as those offered by SyQuest or DAT-type tapes as well as optical drives, are now being used. Each of these storage approaches requires its own proprietary hardware units to record and/or play back. Also, some consideration has to be given as to whether the photographer's choice of storage media is compatible with the particular service bureaus and labs that are going to be supplying the image input and output.

KODAK Photo CD is an excellent medium for image duplication, storage, and viewing. KODAK Pro Photo CD allows copyright information to be paired with each image on a disc. Ultimately sound, text, and graphics will be able to be recorded along with the images so that multimedia presentations can be put together.

In view of these considerations, many digital imaging users have been interested in establishing an industry standard for storage which would tie together the output from scanners and digital cameras and the hardware that runs the various output choices. KODAK Photo CD appears to be a strong contender to address this need.

Basically, KODAK Photo CD carries the digitized information of a film scan on what physically looks like a CD disc as used in music systems, similarly resistant to damage and easy to store. Initially, Kodak marketed Photo CD as primarily a consumer device to enable customers to play back their pictures on the family TV, but it quickly became apparent that professionals were quite interested in its basic characteristics of durability, low cost per unit, and ease of use with simple playback devices. So while much of the KODAK Photo CD packaging and technology are still consumer-oriented, there is also what is called the KODAK Pro Photo CD Master Disc. These discs are capable of storing not only the 35mm images of the consumer version, but larger formats in high resolution as well. Playback units are relatively inexpensive, and the configuration of the CD disc allows for great flexibility in locating and working with images stored on it.

Besides the use of KODAK Photo CD as a primary storage medium for images, this technology lends itself to many other applications. For example, the reduction of pictures to low-resolution "thumbnails" permits the storage of hundreds, even thousands, of pictures on one disc for quick previews as is commonly needed in stock houses. There are also a number of software programs that Kodak has developed to facilitate "search and find" activities, as well as integrating KODAK Photo CD with all of the major image management software programs. Computer manufacturers are also providing for KODAK Photo CD playback in new machines as part of the latest surge of "multimedia" computers that are now becoming so popular.

Thus, the relatively small, easy-to-store, and durable KODAK Photo CD, with its enormous capacity to store images in a variety of ways at different resolutions, appears to be emerging as one of the primary storage media available to photographers working in digital photography today.

Output Options

Once images are committed to digital files, a number of output options become available, many of which are new to photography. The first of these options is, in fact, to return to a silver-based output via a film recorder. Essentially, these devices have extremely high-resolution CRT (cathode ray tube) screens that display the pictures from digital files. Special silver-based films such as KODAK EKTACHROME Electronic Output Film 100, 200, or 64T are then used in conventional cameras to photograph the screens with excellent results. In this manner either negatives or transparencies can be generated and then used just as they would be from regular silver-based films.

Keep in mind, however, that the ability of digital systems to duplicate images without a loss or a shift in contrast, as mentioned earlier, does not extend to the films used to make these copies from a film recorder. Once an image is copied onto film in a film recorder, that on-film image is controlled by the same conventional film restraints discussed earlier in this book. If multiple copies of the digital image are required, the best strategy is to make a new frame of film from the film recorder each time a copy is desired. This will generally yield better results than trying to duplicate the film image made from the CRT screen. At the moment, the output from film recorders goes up to as large as 11 x 14-inch film in either reversal or negative emulsions for color and black and white.

The most popular choice for producing prints directly from the computer right on the desktop is to use a thermal dye transfer printer such as the KODAK XLS 8600 Printer. These prints appear very much like color (or black-and-white) prints when made from large files and on glossy paper stock. They are suitable for use as either proofs or for display and publication. While all of these printers vary in details of their operation, all are based on the depositing of layers of color material from ribbons onto a paper matrix in multiple passes. Heat is then used to literally melt the colors together on the surface and produce the final palette of colors.

Dye sublimation printers can produce photographic-quality output.

Earlier versions of this type of printing, the products of which are often called dye sublimation prints or simply "dye sub prints," were quite prone to scratching with significant fading of the image after very short periods of time. Kodak has greatly improved on these drawbacks by, among other things, coating the print with a protective, clear sheeting. Today's thermal dye transfer prints are quite impressive with a full photographic appearance.

In addition to the output from digital files back to silver via film recorders and producing desktop prints with dye sub printers, there are also a number of other processes available, such as the use of laser-based printers that transfer the digital image to photographic papers using various proprietary photosensitive materials. Some are based on a process that uses pigments instead of dyes, which are much more resistant to fading than any of the color materials used in either electronic or conventional photographic papers.

Finally, there is ink jet technology available from a wide number of manufacturers which is based on spraying droplets as small as 10 microns onto a non-photographic paper surface. This is accomplished through the use of special pumps equipped with jets that have vibrating crystals to modulate the transfer of the colored inks to the matrix or paper surface. These inks are applied in a thin line as the paper, which has been attached to a large drum, rotates at a constant speed and the jets are moved across its surface in a very accurately controlled manner. The result is that the image is literally sprayed onto the paper, one row at time with each row merging to some degree as controlled by the software.

The advantage of this process is the ability to make large prints while preserving image quality. Fine art photographers particularly like this process, especially in a monochrome rendering, because it uses a wide range of papers much like the very old paper-coating technologies of the last century, such as platinum printing. Image quality is photographic but more like one would expect from photographs made on more textured or softer paper surfaces. Ink jet prints, by their nature, have been susceptible to moisture and water damage as well as color fading when displayed for long periods of time. When stored in a dry and totally dark environment, however, ink jet prints are said to last for extremely long periods of time. Also, recent improvements in inks and coating technology hold the promise that this form of printing will be more resistant to moisture and fading.

In closing, the potential for digital photography to change the way photographic copying and duplication is undertaken is wide-ranging and significant. In general, however, the hardware required to carry out this process is very expensive and in many cases, is reserved for service bureaus and larger service labs. At the same time, the cost of setting up high-quality desktop operations is coming down as quality from such setups goes up, and the same is true, to some extent, of digital camera technology. There appears to be little doubt that digital imaging techniques will continue to grow in usage among photographers concerned with duplication and copying techniques. Nevertheless, most experts in the field see an extended period, at least into the next decade, in which both silver halide films and digital photography will coexist, each serving the photographer's needs in their own particular ways.

RECOMMENDED READING

Conservation of Photographs (F-40)

Provides technical and professional information on the stability of both black-and-white and color photographic processes. Recommended for anyone interested in photo preservation and fine-art photography. Covers restoration of deteriorated images, preservation through reproduction, storage, display, and more. Over 145 illustrations. Softbound. 156 pages. 8-1/2 x 11". ISBN 0-87985-352-2 CAT No. E193 5725

Photographic Retouching (E-97)

Provides comprehensive information on the art and science of photographic retouching. Includes sections on tools and materials; black-and-white, color, and color separation negatives; black-and-white and color prints; color transparencies; emulsion stripping; cutting and butting; and more. Over 170 illustrations. Softbound. 116 pages. 8-1/2 x 11". ISBN 0-87985-474-X CAT No. E149 1257

Care and Identification of 19th-Century Photographic Prints (G-2S)

Explains how to identify and care for 19th-century photographic prints. Gives information on the history of photographic processes and identifying types of prints. Also includes a section on storage and display, and the forms of deterioration. Includes a *Care and Identification Flowchart*. Over 125 illustrations. Softbound. 116 pages. 8-1/2 x 11". ISBN 0-87985-365-4 CAT No. E160 7787

KODAK Curve-Plotting Graph Paper (E-64)

KODAK Curve-Plotting Graph Paper provides professional, commercial, and industrial color laboratories with an easy way to plot step-tablet or gray-scale images made on film separations, internegatives, and masks. The semi-transparent paper stock lets you superimpose two or more sheets for easy, direct comparison. 25 sheets. 8-1/2 x 11". CAT No. E146 0369

KODAK Color Print Viewing Filter Kit (R-25)

For evaluating the color balance of prints made from negatives and transparencies. Contains six filter cards: red, green, blue, cyan, magenta, and yellow. Each card has three filters of different densities; 0.10, 0.20, and 0.40. Packed in a durable plastic case with instructions. 5 x 8-3/4". ISBN 0-87985-014-0 CAT No. E150 0735

KODAK Gray Cards (R-27)

Helps you determine exposure, adjust lighting ratio, and check lighting distribution. The gray side has 18% reflectance; the white side has 90% reflectance. Envelope contains two 8 x 10-inch cards and a 4 x 5-inch card, with instructions. ISBN 0-87985-754-4 CAT No. E152 7795

KODAK Professional Black-and-White Films (F-5)

Introduces you to the many varieties and uses of Kodak black-and-white films, with sections on film characteristics and choosing a film. Data section describes Kodak black-and-white films and gives technical information. Also contains a ringaround to help you expose and develop film for optimum density and contrast. Over 40 illustrations. Softbound. 88 pages. 8-1/2 x 11". ISBN 0-87985-651-3 CAT No. E152 8298

KODAK Black-and-White Darkroom DATAGUIDE (R-20)

Provides information on exposing film, controlling development, printing and processing for print stability, and toning. Also includes information and many applications on KODAK T-MAX Professional Films and T-MAX Developers. Over 40 illustrations. Spiral-bound. 66 pages. 6 x 8-1/2". ISBN 0-87985-602-5 CAT No. E828 9092

KODAK Color Darkroom DATAGUIDE (R-19)

Provides practical and in-depth information on processing Kodak color films and papers. Also has information on filters, equipment, and techniques for color printing including a dial for calculating exposure times. There are color ringarounds for evaluating the color balance of prints made from negatives and transparencies. Over 70 illustrations. Spiral-bound. 68 pages. 6 x 8-1/2". ISBN 0-87985-611-4 CAT No. E156 9136

KODAK Professional Photoguide, 5th edition (R-28)

Up-to-date information for producing black-and-white and color photographs; contains data sections on films, exposures, reciprocity, filtration, flash, camera lenses, and perspective. Also includes 29 tables and charts, 8 dial calculators, formulas for making photographic calculations, and an 18% gray card. Spiral-bound. 56 pages. 6 x 8-1/2". ISBN 0-87985-759-5 CAT No. E104 2282

KODAK Photographic Filters Handbook (B-3)

Contains filter information for professional photographers, photo lab technicians, and anyone requiring extensive wavelength-by-wavelength transmission measurements. Includes types of filters and their physical, optical, and transmission characteristics. Over 100 curves. Spiral-bound. 160 pages. 6 x 8-1/2". ISBN 0-87985-658-0 CAT No. E152 8108

Kodak books are available on a wide range of technical and creative photographic topics for both amateurs and professionals. Ask your photo dealer about Kodak books or contact: Silver Pixel Press®, division of The Saunders Group, 21 Jet View Drive, Rochester, NY 14624 Fax: (716) 328-5078